Sharon

A
Harlequin
Romance

OTHER
Harlequin Romances
by MARGARET WAY

STORM
OVER MANDARGI

by

MARGARET WAY

HARLEQUIN BOOKS TORONTO
WINNIPEG

Original hard cover edition published in 1973
by Mills & Boon Limited.

© Margaret Way 1973

SBN 373-01766-9

Harlequin edition published March 1974

1766   Printed in Canada

CHAPTER ONE

It was the quality of the silence that made her nervous and uneasy; more acute than could be imagined, a silence as eerie as an empty vault and twice as ominous. Even the birds and reptilian life had withdrawn to shelter conveying their own message of warning. *Something* was going to happen as it always did in the tropics. There were no kind, easy seasons in the Gulf. The Dry was too dry and the Wet was too wet, heralded by sudden violent wind and rain storms, terrific storm centres that built up over the isolated stations.

Today, none of the usual happy chatter, the soft singing and rhythmic hand-claps issued from the kitchen. Tikka and Leila, the two little aboriginal girls, were all but useless, conquered by the primitive kind of fear that cut deeply into coloured minds, lacing Toni's own blood with a peculiar tension. There was no magic powerful enough to ward off the hot winds of trouble, they told her, their black liquid eyes pools of foreboding. Soon the Big Wind would come, led by Pippimunni, the Lightning Woman, the messenger of the Sky Country.

Toni shrugged off the effects of that harrowing tale. There was no question, they *got* to you, the elemental brown people with their taboos and their spirit links

5

and their strange tribal gods. She eased herself out of the bamboo armchair and walked into the comparative cool of the wide, deep veranda. Its ten-foot shelter ran round two sides of the ninety-year-old bungalow, protecting it from the heat and the heavy onslaughts of monsoonal rain. Banks of flame-coloured lilies, speckled with crimson, ran the full length of the front veranda, their brilliance unbearable in the supercharged air.

Toni leaned her head against the crisscrossed white hardwood pillar, looking out over the large, rambling garden. Another day in the wilderness! The lonely bush, a bitter-sweet isolation, yet it had its own queer magic. She lifted her head to stare at the sinister heat haze that had been threatening to hide the sun since noon. The sun still burned brassily through its numerous veils, invincible, all-possessing, stifling the landscape. It could mean a dry electrical storm, with the shock of thunder but little promise of moisture, but somehow she didn't think so. The atmosphere was heavy with a nameless blend of awe and "rain talk".

No whisper of breeze moved the great shade trees of the garden. They stood engraved, breathless, waiting for the signal. The air was uncannily still, fiery against her cheek, like a blast furnace, causing her eyes to smart and her hair to cling damply in bronze tendrils to her temples and nape. She was almost sick with the heat and mounting anxieties, the core of them Paul's continuing absence. It was nerve-racking to wait, the minutes crawling past at a snail's pace, so that her mind was free to range over all manner of disasters. She was creamy pale, her forehead beaded with perspiration, her dark eyes shadowed in a delicately determined face.

It was well before eleven when Paul had gone out with a few of the stock boys to settle the cattle and turn the restless, sweating beasts to the nearest lagoons and billabongs. Trouble was brewing, he had pointed out laconically, and all forms of life seemed to know it. She remembered his short laugh, the flash of his smile as he rode out to be at least one step ahead of it. Paul could look after himself, none better, but the knowledge did little to comfort her. She sighed, almost beaten by the enervating heat, filled with the curious, useless sensation of marking time. Screwing up her eyes didn't make her brother's form materialise. No lanky lean figure swung into sight, slouched and relaxed in the saddle, blue eyes crinkling in the shade of his hat; a lean boyish face and a bright bronze head tilted at a characteristic angle, absorbed and confident.

Paul was no ordinary young man and he didn't propose to lead an uneventful life. He had certain set targets, the first of them, *Mandargi* the bright dream, the four-hundred-square-mile property he managed for Damon Nyland, a man of immense property interests and the owner of the big experimental station Savannah Downs on their north-eastern border. Toni had never met the great man, as she very quickly dubbed

7

him. The master of Mandargi had never set foot on his property in the whole six months since she had left her job and a go-nowhere romance to come north and join her brother and run the domestic affairs of the station for him. But she heard Nyland's praises sung ad nauseam; at the few hectically gay social gatherings, in the township, from buyers and agents, cattlemen and their womenfolk, markedly a-twitter. No one loomed larger upon the horizon, casting a long shadow, than the exclusive, elusive Damon Nyland, with a name guaranteed to keep one listening.

Toni, ever the individualist, often felt inclined to tip her forehead in a simple, respectful form of homage every time she heard his name. Instead, in order to make a contribution, she listened with an air of pleasant interest, trying to look appreciative as though Nyland's exploits made her think very deeply. Even in the seclusion of the wilds, man must have his idols. Once or twice it crossed her mind to question the illogical antagonism she seemed to have settled into without a qualm, but lacking the interest, was forced back on the old standby; the man's telltale activities, the tangible and tantalising aura of dynamism that clung to a name. Damon Nyland was quite simply a big wheel, a man of prestige and power, the kind of man "the State could well do with" as she'd read somewhere in the newspaper and put it down very smartly. One could hardly expect such a man to dance attendance on his run-of-the-mill employees. He had a reason for everything he did. For her own part, there was no harm at all in being prepared. She wasn't going to fall on the great man's neck. All this reverence and mutterings of approval touched some perverse nerve in her.

Paul, on the other hand, wouldn't hear a word against his employer, bristling unaccountably at Toni's mocking jibes so that after a while, she learnt to go quietly, feeling herself as wise as an ancient spirit grandmother, twenty-two to her brother's twenty-seven. Her tender mouth was compressed, giving an indication of what lay behind her thoughts. Even Damon Nyland would be awed by the primeval quality of this vast, empty land, the weird quicksilver effects of the heat haze. She nibbled on her underlip with growing disquiet, her eyes on the frowning, ragged line of the ranges, purple and blue ramparts rising against the sky. The peculiar subtlety of the silence was penetrating to her bones, making her turn away with a forlorn little gesture hoping that Paul would beat the storm in. It would be a long, hot ride.

At three o'clock, great curling cumulus cloud came up from nowhere, purple-black laced with silver and green at the edges, crossing the horizon with great speed like an angry tide in reverse. Toni gauged the ceiling height at about six thousand feet and there could be a similar depth of cloud cover indicating heavy turbulence and electrical surcharge. She watched the swift, oncoming masses from inside the battened-down house, her blood stirred to fever heat. Behind her on the wicker sofa sat Tikka and Leila, in crippling insecurity, their slight arms entwined, speechless with their dreaded, psychic terrors. Soon the wind would blow up with great force and Paul wasn't in. Toni felt her own stomach muscles knotting with her sheer inability to do anything about it. Everything seemed to be waiting for the storm to take over.

Within minutes the sun went out, obliterated by the fantastic cloud barriers. Lightning forked through the pearly-black mounds, brilliant, and quite terrifying, sizzling with livid fury into the huge coolibah that stood at the end of the pebbled drive. It split asunder like so much matchwood, falling in the darkened, wind-swept landscape, endlessly resounding, rocking the bungalow to its foundations and sending birds screeching; shadows of kites and eagles and falcons, the shrieking sulphur-crested cockatoos and the rose-pink galahs almost helpless against the force of the wind.

Toni shook her head dazedly, not even knowing she was doing it. The spell of unearthly quiet was broken. All hell broke loose with amazing rapidity. The first giant spatters of rain came down on the corrugated iron roof like a fusillade of artillery, then a driving deluge mixed with the lethal hail; massive chunks of ice as large as emu's eggs. Small forms of bush life, half blinded by the rain and flying gravel, streaked eratically across the garden only to be killed or maimed by the icy grenades that ricocheted off a bigger animal to strike yet another in its frantic flight. Toni shut her eyes, her face paper-white, her ears assaulted by the deafening racket on the roof, yet her fears were not for herself nor the homestead, but her brother. Hail like that was dangerous to man and beast. The cattle so carefully mustered would be petrified by the storm, moaning horribly, stampeding to the densest scrub, dangerous in their panic.

She couldn't bear to look out at that beautiful barbaric scene or listen to the savage throbbing of the wind and rain. Strange that so much beauty could come out of so much terror. The two little aboriginal housegirls were moaning now with a paralysing sense of calamity, their curly black heads bowed. All about them, along the exposed side of the bungalow, came the splintering break of glass as windows shattered and blew in, drenching large areas in minutes.

Leila's explosive scream, like a train whistle, quickly choked off to an abject whimper as Toni silenced her without speaking a word, her velvety winged brows drawn down in alarmed exasperation. She'd endured enough of this. Something had to be done, she was tired of coping with such enforced inertia. She tilted her head, the muscles under the young curve of her chin tightening in a quick acceptance of possible disaster. Would the roof hold under the ramming force of the hail or give way before the storm had spent itself? Resolution seized her. She ran on through the house to the study with its massive buffalo horns mounted over the door, but her attention was all for the radio transceiver. It stood on the desk between two shovel-nosed spears fixed to the window wall. She almost flung herself into the swivel chair, threw the switch, pushed the send button on the mike, gave the station's call-sign. "This is MTW . . . Mandargi. . . ."

Then as she drew in her breath sharply, the whole window frame seemed to plunge for her. There was a harsh splitting sound, then something hit her and the world went black.

Something's happened, she told herself. Something's happened to me. She lay there, a warm and sticky sensation crawling over her skin. A long way off, a dog barked. It was Rebel, she was almost sure of it. Rebel! Then Paul was back! The sound seemed to hang on in the air. She opened her eyes suddenly, with a small, bewildered exclamation. It was still, so very still, she could hear the thud of her heart. She turned her head, her dark eyes flickering, and it all came back to her. She was lucky. All about her was chaos. Scattered, drenched books and papers; an upturned chair and a fan ripped out of the wall. Splintered glass lay like a giant diadem around her head and the shattered window-frame half across her body. She could remember the moment of impact like a pistol shot in her head.

Blood was all over the side of her shirt and the sight made her sick and nauseated beyond belief. It was only then that she became conscious of a violent headache

and a searing pain in her arm. She looked down dazedly, unsurprised by the bad gash on the inside of her
right arm. It must have happened as she flung it up
instinctively to protect herself. She lay still for a few
more moments, then she made a supreme effort to
raise herself, only to fall back as black waves of sick-
ness threatened to ride her down. Ridiculous! She was
almost too weak to move. She ran a tentative hand
down her arm and felt the stickiness of blood. She
swallowed, her eyes widening.

Where were the girls? The Missy would be dead for
sure! That would be their unanimous verdict, their
black eyes enormous, in small frightened faces, perched on the fine edge of hysteria. They had a deep-seated
fear of death, the final crisis in the life cycle, suffi-
cient to keep them well clear of the study until the Master came home. Even in the midst of the critical circumstances she found herself in, Toni had a moment
of wry humour. Well, the Missy was far from dead.
No bones broken either. Just a rather deep wound and
a bad crack on the head.

The storm was over with the abruptness of all
tropical storms, the rain turned off as suddenly and
completely as a tap. A steady flow of washed-clean air
was coming in through the great, open gap where the
window had been. Perhaps it would serve to sober her
up. She bit her lip and turned an ivory pale face towards the cool after-rush of the storm, almost in the
same moment passing out.

She opened her eyes. She felt better, almost comfortable, lying on the old black leather sofa in the lounge room, staring into a face. Dark, disturbing, different. She knew that face.

"Welcome back!" he said sardonically, and the voice matched the face.

Toni didn't say anything; her eyes roamed over his face as though condemned to look at it for the rest of her life. Various expressions – irony, ease, authority. Ice-green eyes that seemed to mesmerize her so that she blinked a little, irritated by the discovery. Then faint spirit returned to her.

"Well put!" she murmured with a ghost of her usual delicate mockery. "How long *have* I been out?"

"You were unconscious when I arrived about half past five. And," he glanced at his watch, "it's now seven o'clock!"

"Good grief!" she said soberly, her face tautening. "Where's Paul? Where's my brother?"

"Paul's all right!" he underlined crisply with an air of finality, watching the agitation mount in her face. "He's looked in several times, now he's gone out again. *You're* the patient! Apart from the concussion, that was a bad gash in your arm. I've put in a few stitches. Don't talk, if you please!" he added tersely, his mouth hardening, evidently unused to the faint mutiny he saw in her face.

"And if I don't please?" She eased out her breath

rather painfully, wincing at the first incautious movement of her arm.

"I can't say I wasn't expecting it!" he said, studying
her, his eyes gleaming with a kind of, I know you, but
you don't know me, superiority. "Even out cold, you
betray a certain nervous intensity. One way and the
other, it's been a devil of a day. I suppose it's too late
telling you, you should never have come up here. The
wrong temperament — too volatile for the tropics.
You'll wear yourself out!"

"Not quite!" she replied, with self-mockery, not
bothering to hide her thoughts from him. She returned
his gaze, her dark eyes critical and appraising but
scarcely hostile. A man like that would always take
one's breath away. One had to be braced for almost
anything, and her recuperative powers had always been
good. "Perhaps it was worth it, just to meet you ...
Mr. Nyland, isn't it." It was hardly a question and
he responded briefly to the point of curtness.

"Yes!"

"Strange, to remain unimpressed!" It was out in
one awful minute before her head cleared, triggered by
that taut monosyllable. But what did he expect? A
song of joy and welcome! He seemed to, for his green
eyes glittered like a flame sprung to life and she knew
a stab of pure panic. She had gone too far, and what
did she really know of him? However, his voice, when
it came, was a smooth drawl, brushing aside her neglig-
ible opinions.

15

"You'll get over it! In fact, once you accept your change of environment, you may even learn a healthy respect!"

She turned her head from the brilliance of his strange eyes, his dark face controlled. "Are you warning me?"

"Of course!"

"Then I suppose I deserved it!" A smile touched her mouth and she fingered the bandage around her arm, realising for the first time that she owed him a good deal, this local autocrat by his own admission. "For what it's worth, Mr. Nyland, I apologise. It's a failing of mine, charging in where angels fear to tread!"

"The hit on the head, or perhaps you're nervous?" His gaze was cool and faintly amused.

"Nervous?" She shrugged that off delicately, but she was still wary of him. It would be impossible for him to forgive her impertinence however well he concealed it. Reprisals at some stage would be second nature to him.

He was looking at her directly, his eyes playing lightly over her face, and she felt oddly shaken as if she were moving in a new element. "As well as talking too much!" he said smoothly. "A charming weakness in a woman. It's a good thing I can see beyond all the bravado and you *have* had a time of it. One must make allowances!"

Her voice was low and faintly husky in the quiet

emptiness of the room. Ridiculous to think of him as an adversary, yet the sensation persisted. "You have a very direct way with you, Mr. Nyland!"

"So have you! It must be catching!"

"I don't imagine I'm quite so . . . *disconcerting*, but thank you for this," she gestured to her bandaged arm "and for coming. It must have been quite a risk!"

"You're welcome!"

"But the storm . . . ?"

"As you can see, I'm here!" he said crisply, chopping her off. "It's not important for you to know all the details!"

"No, of course not. Why should I trouble my sweet little head?" She was rambling a little, her voice faintly slurred. Her dark eyes, shadowed in the pallor of her face, struggled to hold his, but those strongly defined features were blurring. It worried her. The room swung in her view and a sickening wave of giddiness passed over her. "I think I'm going to faint!" she murmured with something like horror.

He gave a faint sigh more sardonic than sympathetic. "Suits me, you'll be easier to handle!" His mouth twisted in a smile. She felt his hands touch her – sure, very certain. "A beautiful piece of timing. A true feminine gift! Relax, child, there's nothing whatever to worry about!" Then he was lifting her, cradling her with no effort at all, protective of her arm, flicking down at her a mocking smile that still held a degree of indulgence.

Lights seemed to be bursting under her eyelids. There were so many questions she wanted to ask. Why wasn't Paul there? She didn't want to go with this stranger at all, for all she accepted his presence as an entirely natural thing. But all she could manage was a soft, plaintive cry, the tears of weakness beading her lashes. Clouds of cottonwool were suffocating her. She tried to slant a glance at that lean, hard jaw, the infernal tilt to a night-dark head, then she slid into darkness again.

CHAPTER TWO

She awoke very early from a deep sleep. She had no more than a faint headache and a heavy sensation in her right arm, turning her face towards the mother-of-pearl light. On the dawn wind, soft singing came from the direction of the willow-hung billabong, wafting in through the bungalow windows. A song of an old, old race, a woman chant to attract the goodwill of the spirit folk. Toni listened, moved and enchanted, still so new to all that was alien and exotic about the far north. Her wandering eyes moved drowsily about the room. Not much she had been able to do about it, her bedroom, except re-paint the old tongue-and-groove walls in a pale blue colour with a glossy white trim, along with the odd bits of old-fashioned furniture in an effort to match them together. The curtains, the cushions, the bedspread, in a vibrant contemporary print, she made herself, an attractive enough contribution, as were the few favourite ornaments she had brought with her. But it was essentially an unpretentious room, of modest proportions, clinically cool and fresh, and no amount of know-how and imagination could make it brilliant. With a view like hers of feathery, magnificent poincianas and the distant grape-blue of the ranges she could do with big, beautiful, airy windows, but through the single multi-paned window she could hardly see anything. At least the glass in it wasn't shattered. Still under the effects of the sedative, she closed her eyes and drifted off again.

The first rays of sunlight slanted dusky-gold, through the venetian blinds, falling across the bed. Their warmth stirred her. She looked up at the pale canopy of tropical netting that enveloped her and kicked the light sheet from her legs, looking down the length of her elegant young body. Her right arm was bandaged in a very professional fashion, an incongruous note, for she was wearing an exquisite froth of nylon and lace in a muted coffee shade; a birthday present from their unfailingly romantic maiden aunt and one she had no recollection of ever taking out of its box, scorning its obvious lack of practicality. Clearly some hours of her life were missing. She would never have chosen it herself.

She remembered the storm, the series of incidents

that led to the one wholly unexpected development —
the appearance of Damon Nyland. One more shock in
a series of shocks. She knew with some certainty he
was a man she would clash with. Her awakening mind
raced ahead, foreseeing the difficulties, almost ticking
off points on her fingers. Much better to do the fashion-
able thing and fall down adoring, but she couldn't see
herself doing it. The man already had more followers
than a tribal chief. Uncompromising masculinity had
always set her teeth on edge, a physical aversion that
made her feel vaguely uncomfortable. It was unsettling, that peculiar blend of charm and hard arrogance.

Her mouth tilted in faint self-mockery. Lying so
quietly, it was not necessary to suppress her thoughts,
so she let them run on. Seen in the light of cold reason, the answer was simple enough — avoid the man.
It shouldn't prove difficult, if only a crisis merited a
visit. Hard as she tried to disavow the idea, she had to
admit he played his part with enormous conviction —
a strong suggestion of the *grand seigneur* with perhaps
a streak of cruelty thrown in. Extraordinarily im-
pressive and profoundly attractive. Men out of the
ordinary mould were dangerous. Damon Nyland, as
such, was a natural suspect, but such knowledge was
better kept in reserve.

Surely she wasn't becoming cynical?

She'd never really been hurt by a man. A few rapid
charades with little time for understanding on either
side. No stars that fell from the skies. No love lost at

all. In fact, she knew very little about love.

Strange how a dark face lodged in her mind. Skin a deep copper, the shock of light eyes, cool as mint, glints in a thick twist of black hair. Her mouth curved with irony and sweetness, visualising the odd six-monthly encounter when he invariably came off second-best. Some men wore an air of bright challenge impossible to ignore. At least she was lucky in having an inbuilt warning system, one that could sum up dark, impatient men at a glance.

Morning sounds broke through her imaginings; the beautiful, carolling bird-song, lilting aboriginal voices, the sound of someone sweeping up the pebbles in the drive. Quite near the house Rebel barked and was immediately shushed by a very loud voice with the crazy notion it couldn't be heard. Toni smiled with deep amusement, feeling a wave of love for her brother. Even his voice had an eagerness and glow in it that promised well for his future. She didn't appreciate fully that she and her brother were identical in many ways; ways that were apparent to even the most casual observer. The bright bronze heads, the clean bone structure, shapely, sensitive mouths with the half-smile each wore. The inner excitement was there and the lively intelligence, only Paul's eyes were blue and Toni's darkly brilliant, but the light challenge shone from both, reflected in the rather audacious tilt to their heads.

In another minute, Paul tapped on her door, scarcely

waiting for her bright, answering: "Come in!"

He walked into the room with swinging grace, smiling at her. "Rebel woke you, I suppose. I looked in on you earlier and your colour was good. How do you feel now?"

"Not too bad. Bit of a head and this feels heavy, but I suppose it's the bandage." She fingered it tentatively.

He nodded and came to sit on the end of the bed, anxiously scanning her face. "Honestly, if anything else had happened to you, I'd have to crawl away and die of grief!"

"How fantastic!" she smiled.

"No one could help liking you. Anyway, you gave me an awful fright. Savannah picked up your call sign and the Boss flew in. Damned good of him! He's a big man and they don't usually do that kind of thing!"

"Oh, I don't know!" she pointed out brightly, "business men have been known to protect their property interests. Still, it must be marvellous to be admired!"

Paul raised his eyebrows and kicked at the rug. "You'll never do. Too much spunk. Here's my story . . . Mack's horse came down in a melon hole and rolled on him. He's broken his leg, I'm afraid – Mack, not the horse. The horse I can spare, not Mack, the careless ass, the only word I can find for him. By the way, the Flying Doctor is due in this morning. He'll take a look at you at the same time. I tell you, girl, some days it just doesn't pay to fall out of bed. My best man out of action, and the cattle spread out to the four winds!"

"Not to speak of your sister! I've been wondering why you called in. At any rate, *I* intend to stay in bed all day, not moving!"

Paul made a snorting sound and ran a hand over his head. "I should say so! The Boss would have my hide if you tried to get up today. But what's a few teeth more or less? He's fairly certain you won't have a scar. The prettiest, neatest job I've ever seen."

"Don't tell me the great man's still here?" she asked in amazement.

"Of course. He's going to take a good look over the place — a report on my stewardship, no less. Now that you're awake, I'll get a few of the boys to clean up the debris about the place. We've a few too many windows to replace and little time to spend on them."

"Well, now that we *do* have to replace them, let's make them bigger!"

He gave her a look that could have been approval. "Anything you say, you're the Missus."

"Until you marry!" she answered him carelessly, unprepared for his swift double-take.

"Who, me?" He stood up, squaring his straight shoulders. "Not of my own free will, anyway. No woman is going to get me in her clutches until I'm good and ready!"

"That's what they all say!" she murmured dryly.

23

"I'll remind you of it when the time comes. By the way, how did I get into this fabulous gear?"

He smiled in amusement, enjoying the moment, proud of his sister's good looks. "Tikka, who else? Now why don't you give it to her? That would be a nice gesture. Think of the repercussions. Plenty woman-magic, and you don't particularly need it. Poor little beggar thought you were dead, you know. She nearly went white when I asked her to help you out of your clothes. More like a mortuary rite. But there's no doubt about it, she has a great sense of what's suitable. That's some nightie. Trust poor old Rose – four times round the world and not one proposal! Now, if you're sure you're all right, I'll get going. You never catch up with the work on a station and I've the feeling Nyland's not the man to keep waiting." He walked to the door, pulling a wry face over his shoulder. "He certainly took charge last night!"

"Who got here first?" she called after him, trying to sound detached and disinterested. "I remember precious little, flaking out all the time."

"The Boss beat me in by about forty minutes. Hauled me over the coals a bit, but what the devil! Superman wouldn't have risked that hail!"

"Nyland did!" she pointed out, her affectionate smile contradicting the tart note in her voice.

"He flew *over* it, dear. The bright spirit. Do try to be fair. Besides, the storm was over almost as soon as it'd begun. Just as well! – the roof took a battering.

24

I've some work there. Poor old Mack bit the dust long before the storm broke. He's so damned mad with himself none of the boys are game to go near him. It was you or him and I thought you would be safe enough. I just hauled him to shelter and sat it out. Jimmy D. left the ute out, and it's pitted with holes. I'll skin him alive if he's ever game to come back again. It was his job to bring it in, but it's the same old story, if you want a job done . . . Well, make the most of it, girl," he flashed his white smile, already preoccupied, "I need your assistance around here. Those two little twits in the kitchen go to the pack without direction. It's not the work that appeals to them. Lord only knows what we had for breakfast. Even the Boss didn't ask. Didn't eat it either!"

"Dear me!" she said, the tart note back in her voice again. "I guess he'll survive!"

"So will you," he reminded her. "You were losing a fair amount of blood."

"I'm ashamed of myself!"

"That'll be the day! So long, kiddo!" He moved swiftly away. "Back before lunch."

"I only hope Mr. Nyland will like it!" her voice floated after him, almost triumphant.

For a little while after he left, Toni savoured the comfort of the soft, old-fashioned bed, conscious of a dull ache in her head. She threw up a hand to shield her eyes from the bright sunlight. A slanting shaft fell across her thick, silky hair, lighting it to a radiance,

25

flashing out all the bright reds and the ambers. She would give herself a little while longer, then she would get up. Extraordinarily privileged as they were with Damon Nyland on the premises, it wouldn't do to be laid low at the first impact. Less than one hundred per cent.

Tikka, moving along the hallway, tray in hand, let out a soft cry as a teaspoon clattered to the polished floor. Toni sat up, giving all thoughts of relaxation away, watching the little aboriginal girl in her best blue housedress move slowly into sight. She took one look at Toni and gave a short gasp, her black eyes enormous in her small dusky face, her features finer than most of her people.

"You're awake, Miss Toni?" For some reason she spoke in a near whisper and Toni smiled, entertained.

"Happily, yes!" she said positively. "Hours ago. Is that breakfast? It's a cup of tea I want more than anything else!"

"Tea it is!" Tikka was thinking hard. She came into the room and placed the tray on the bedside table, fussing a little over the important business of pouring the tea. "Lucky you're still here, Miss Toni. I thought you wuz dead!"

Toni shook her bright head. "You were about half way right! *Dead?* What next?"

Tikka suddenly giggled, pointing a finger at the coffee lace nightgown. "I could work all me life for something like that!"

26

Toni glanced down wryly, moving her long, slender legs, tanned to a deep gold, beautifully conspicuous beneath the short, foaming hemline. "It's yours if you want it that badly. It makes me feel like a cross between a Botticelli lady and a racehorse!"

Tikka drew in her breath hoarsely as if she needed air. "*Mine*? That's rockin' the boat a bit. I don't know what Albert would say, but I'd feel like Sheba!"

Toni laughed aloud. "Apes and peacocks and ivory thrones!" A persuasive look came over her face. "Surely Albert wouldn't see it. Not yet, anyway. It might pay to keep that in mind!"

Tikka looked back at her rather helplessly, caught between being fickle and devout. "When Mr. Paul promotes Albert, we're goin' to be married!" It came out with great deliberation to hide the wobble of emotion.

"So the rewards will be great! If I were you, Tikka, I'd have no compunction. A wedding present, if you like. Think it over."

Tikka plucked a flower from the vase on the table and waved it in some agitation under her face. "I'll talk myself out of it for sure. I'd be too scared to wear it."

"Because of Albert?" Toni reached for her tea and a finger of toast.

"Sort of!" Tikka explained haltingly. She took a jerky step backwards, not without a quaint grace. "More . . ." Something in her face looked utterly de-

27

fenceless, a denial of some basic fulfilment. She left it up in the air, without an explanation.

Toni smiled at her lightly, with affection. "I think I know what you mean. One way or the other we're all captives of what life hands us out!"

"And it's not fair!" Tikka shifted her weight to the other foot, standing like a stork at a waterhole. She looked to Toni for confirmation, but Toni only smiled.

"In any case, it *is* rather grand – the nightgown, I mean. One needs the right setting and certainly to be happily married. The chances are you'll make it with Albert. I hope so."

"He's crazy about me!" Tikka said, and paused for effect. There wasn't any. Toni finished her cup of tea, then turned and sat up.

"Officially, I'm supposed to spend the day in bed, but unofficially I'm getting up shortly. See what's left of the vegetable garden, would you? The talent I threw into it – and for what? One good hailstorm and annihilation! I daren't ask if either of you two girls brought the tomatoes in, not to speak of all those beautiful lettuce!"

"I surely did!" Tikka clenched her hands in her lap, her face self-righteous.

"Splendid! I'm spellbound," Toni said in her normal voice. "The best thing you've ever done – and to think I questioned your efficiency!"

Tikka looked up quickly, very earnest, her curly black head cocked to one side. "Yesterday was bad.

28

Bad of me, I mean. I'm sorry, Miss Toni. I nebber felt so scared!" Remembrance made her expression crumble and Toni, under the burden of that glance, answered swiftly before the apology misfired.

"Forget it, Tikka. We're all frightened of something or other. Often things we can't explain. I, for instance, would hesitate to make a pet of a snake."

"Catch 'em by the tail. Simple!" Tikka explained.

Toni shuddered, considering the consequences, then she gestured to the tray. "Take this back to the kitchen, like a good girl. Mr. Nyland is here for a while, so there's work to be done!"

"Yes, ma'am!" Tikka smiled, displaying her beautiful teeth. "That sounds just fine! He's a big man!"

"He's certainly tall!" Toni conceded, and wisely changed the subject. "Now, about the vegetable garden, we'll rebuild in stages. I'm not sure if we won't even hire a few men – Albert, for instance. He might welcome the opportunity to work nearer the house for a day or two."

"As long as Albert's about, everything will go all right!" Tikka promised, pure unalloyed pride and delight in her face.

"Good, then it's all planned. Fixed in my mind." Toni relaxed her back, enjoying the lassitude of the moment.

"Shall I get that lazy Leila movin'? Don't know what's eatin' her. She took two hours to get breakfast and then no one eat it!" Tikka looked across at the small Missus with an obvious desire to please.

"Yes, you do that," Toni nodded, fighting the impulse to laugh.

"Right, miss!" Tikka looked hard at the tray, rehearsing her lines, then she looked up and smiled. "I'm sure glad you're all right! Nebber did tell you the Big Boss breathed hell-fire all over us, Leila and me. But we were so scared. I thought you wuz dead and Leila nebber think at all!" The black eyes glinted with merry racial humour. "I'll go and chat up that girl! See you, miss!"

Toni watched the slight figure disappearing, then she began to laugh softly. She would have given a pretty penny to hear what Tikka had to say. Out in the kitchen, anything could happen and often did, but Tikka was, unquestionably, the dominant personality. Breakfast didn't bear thinking about, but she would have to supervise the lunch. If Tikka was to be believed, at least there was enough for a salad.

Thoughts of a menu began to claim her attention. What could she give the man, used as he was to perfection? Grilled chops and spicy grilled pineapple rings with a tossed salad? There was plenty of cold beer. Freshly caught barramundi barbecued on the spot might be the answer. She could stuff it with breadcrumbs and a mixture of seasoned chopped boiled eggs and anchovies. It seemed only fair to make up for lost ground. Even Tikka had admitted that breakfast was a disaster.

There was still a residue of pain and discomfort in her body and brain, but on this day of grace she was determined not to remain in bed. The master of Mandargi was in residence, for however short a duration. Toni kicked the sheet aside and her long legs flashed enticingly, neat and quick as a cat. She turned to grope for her cotton robe and the sunlight fell in a silky gold stream over her young face and bare shoulders, gilding the bright, matchless bronze of her hair. She looked at that moment a fragile, rather exotic beauty with the piquant touch of a bandaged arm.

A man halted in the open doorway, studying her with relaxed interest, the cadence of his voice betraying amused appreciation.

"Good morning, Miss Stewart. About to disobey orders!"

As usual was implied, but not said. Toni swung her head, looking confused and briefly shocked, and he knew it. The fluid grace of her body seemed to vanish as she stiffened, her back as taut as a bow string, clutching the printed robe defensively. He swung the door wider, the swift brilliance of his eyes moving over her, experienced and detached as if she were a fine piece of glass – a unique piece, from the quality of that light, probing glance.

Colour stirred in her cheeks, a sensuous curve to her mouth. If he continued to look at her in that precise fashion she would surely fall in fragments at his feet.

"Mr. Nyland!" she returned with equal smoothness. "This *is* a privilege! I'm bound to say I wasn't expecting you."

"Nor I you!" he countered, closing the distance between them, giving her a minute to slip her arms into the robe and gather it about her. "Why don't you hop back into bed?" he suggested. "You're rather precariously balanced at the moment!"

She made no attempt to rise to that jibe, but watched him lower his long length into a chair with an air of possession and utter familiarity, a rather stunning nonchalance. "May I sit down?" he asked with mild sarcasm. "Now I'm here, I'm looking forward to a little chat. How do you feel this morning?"

"Fine. Just fine!" she said warily, reacting to an odd note in his voice. "Ordinarily I'd curtsy!"

He seemed amused, the cool green glints in his eyes again. "I'm trying to decide whether to make you or not. That nightgown is pure fairy tale, Rose-Red."

"You can't condemn me for that!" Colour swept into her face and she tilted her chin trying to ignore it. "It was a present."

He received that in silence, then laughed. "Really? Then that explains it. It's not the sort of thing one expects to see in the wilds. Neither are you, for that matter. Good-looking women don't usually bury themselves."

"If you could call it that!" Her dark eyes sparkled a challenge. "But tell me, Mr. Nyland, what really brings you away from your office? Did it catch fire?"

"I didn't expect such charm, either!" He laughed in his throat. "Apologise!"

"I can't. My head aches," she said shortly.

"Plus your arm," he said sympathetically. "That bandage gives an engaging but entirely misleading impression of . . . helplessness!"

She flushed a little under that quick lick of green fire. Above the masculine severity of his bush shirt, his darkly tanned face appeared very handsome and vital. Classic really, she thought, determined to be fair. High cheekbones, interesting hollows. Straight nose. Good mouth and a decisive chin. It was the kind of face you wanted to keep looking at, exciting yet inexplicably familiar. She knew with a great certainty that something was starting for her, but she scarcely knew what to call it.

"Let's change the subject," she said pleasantly, "if only to avert a scene!"

"Why not? You won't admit it, but you're the type to hit out at the first one to come along. I got it with both barrels as soon as I came through the door. Why do you dislike me so much? May I ask?" The tiny smile that touched the corners of his mouth both mocked and pitied her.

"Dislike you?" She uttered the words with such cool surprise that her self-esteem came back. "But I don't dislike you at all, Mr. Nyland. In fact I'm covered in admiration!"

"Now why should I have imagined it?" He tipped

back precariously in the chair, very self-assured, his lean body faultlessly arranged. "Perhaps it was the effect of the shot I gave you. You had quite a bit to say last night!"

She drew a deep breath, startled, a topaz sheen caught in her eyes.

"Careful! it's coming pretty close to the surface again!" he warned her. "You were quite funny really, rambling most of the time, but I got the general drift. One piece of news, good or bad I can't say. The strip won't take a plane for the next forty-eight hours or so, so you're stuck with me. It shouldn't bother you unduly, you won't be allowed up in any case. I've been on to the Flying Doctor base for instructions. You're not the only casualty, but you're the one under observation for a while!"

"Do you mean to tell me I'm not allowed up?"

"That's right!" he said repressively.

"Well, who would have thought it?" she said in a low, mocking voice. "Twenty-two and I'm still a baby, but if you want it that way, Mr. Nyland, there's no more to be said."

"I want it that way." It was a plain statement of fact that she could accept and obey. She lifted her eyes and encountered his very direct gaze and a strange perverse excitement moved in her. How idiotic to ride the see-saw of attraction and antagonism. It would be folly to allow herself to like him. It simply wasn't safe. But what exciting man was ever safe?

"I feel perfectly all right, you know," she said swiftly, to cover her confusion.

Her tensions must have communicated themselves to him, for he smiled, poised yet wary. "I'm sure you do!" he nodded, his eyes narrowing, "but you mightn't feel quite so well if you started racing about again. I know how anxious you are to impress me. And I *am* impressed! You've worked wonders on the house since I last saw it – curtains and cushions, rugs and whatnots, floral arrangements and bookcases. You're by no means the usual showpiece." The glance that slid over her was keen and amused.

Something about him, the set of his head and shoulders, the ironic amusement that deepened the curve to his mouth, awoke a faint apprehension in her. But for what? It was difficult to achieve any degree of normality.

"I can see it's going to be horribly difficult!" she said passionately.

"So stop fighting me!" he laughed in genuine amusement. "You can't expect me to encourage this schoolgirl animosity. What was it you said? King of the castle. Master of Mandargi. The great man and the rest." His voice was dangerously soft and Toni got an intimation of what to expect should she ever really cross him. She drew an audible breath, wondering what else she had said, and just as suddenly he was the Big Boss again, very crisp and to the point. "Now, let's have a look at that arm. Not a bad job, if I say so myself! I certainly haven't heard anything from *you*. The unkindest cut of all, if you'll forgive the pun!" Professionally he bent over her arm and she felt herself draw away a little, a new tension bearing down on her. His glance raked over her and his bearing altered just enough for her to resurrect a surviving sense of caution. She fixed her attention on a small pearly button near his lean brown throat.

"A pity to leave a scar on this silky skin," he said lightly, "but it shouldn't be much. Marvellous to be young and healthy. Healing begins almost immediately. We won't disturb anything for the moment. I'll change the dressing this afternoon." He was looking down at her in his own arrogant fashion, head up, eyes narrowing.

"You're a man of many accomplishments, Mr. Nyland!"

"Don't I have to be?" he retorted, hard and direct.

"And a millionaire to boot, if the papers are to be believed!"

"You might remember, in the process, a few people get rich along with me, and quite a lot of *other* people depend on me for their livelihood."

"Oh, I'll remember!" She reached up a hand and thrust it through her hair. "Message received and understood, never fear."

His mouth suddenly relaxed its tension, his teeth very white against his deeply tanned skin. "You never got smacked enough as a child. Too pretty for your

36

own good, I suppose. Never mind, the day of retribution is at hand!"

"I'm sure of it!" she said without hesitation. "I can't help thinking I don't deserve it, but this is *your* country, not mine, Mr. Nyland."

"Terrifying, isn't it?" he countered, standing up and whisking the chair back a few feet. "At least, it's a great help to get acquainted. Now suppose you atone for your past misdemeanours and lie back. I'll organise the staff for the rest of the day. I'm an old hand at it."

"I'm grateful!" Carefully she made her voice blank, fighting her resentments.

"Now *that*, I find incredible. Right at this moment I'd say you're seething, you ungrateful brat!"

"My attempt to curry favour didn't quite come off!" Despite herself she smiled, and his eyes dwelt on her mouth.

"It would seem not, but keep trying. By the way, was that your first storm yesterday?"

"In the tropics, yes."

"You'll get over them," he promised with complete unconcern. "Everything up here is so much more unpredictable. Savage in every way!"

"I'm not frightened!" she said, controlling the few nervous tremors.

"No, you're not, are you, and you *should* be," he murmured with dry mockery. "That's the red hair. A mixed blessing!" His eyes slipped away from her lustrous head. "Well, I'll push on. There are a few other things that can wait. If I were you, I'd try taking it easy. An indispensable attribute in this climate!"

She watched him move to the door with his lithe, effortless paces. "Meeting you has been an unforgettable experience, Mr. Nyland," she said, yielding to a fatal impulse for mischief.

"For which you'll get no more than a simple thank-you. For the present!" He paused, one hand on the door knob, something indefinable glinting in his eyes, "There's plenty of time for drama, if that's what you want!"

She gave an involuntary gasp, tingles of warmth running down her arms. He left her feeling young and uncomfortable and badly outmanoeuvred. At best, it would be an unequal struggle, but she was determined to hold out as long as she could. With practice she might be able to achieve a degree of immunity. Like throwing up a wall between them, yet she was haunted by the thought that he was about to wreck everything. Perhaps she should never have miscast herself to the extent of imagining there was a place for her up here. There was no place for her in the city either, not in the seven long years since their father had remarried. Mandargi was a hundred times better than sharing a flat with two other girls; a monthly duty visit home, the line of least resistance, that placated her father and exhausted Myra's limited supply of feigned good fellowship. More frequent trips would only have proved troublesome all round.

In the early days of the marriage when things were pretty desperate with Myra's jealous possessiveness, Paul had very smartly left home, leaving Toni to go quietly mad with the loneliness of it all. As soon as she was able, she too had fled the nest, as Myra put it, "with largely herself to blame". A survivor of many lone battles, where words hit like blows, Toni kept her stock of grim stories to herself. Her father would scarcely have credited them in any case. A young girl, however high-spirited, was no match for a mature woman who knew when to pick her times.

It had been difficult, but she got through, possibly in the process strengthening her character. When Paul had written, so many months ago: "Come up and really see the sun set!" it came at a time when the circumstances of her life demanded a change. She had gone ahead making arrangements, swiftly withdrawing from the old life, the social round, Martin, who promised her a fixed way of life and a certain success. She had never looked back, or regretted the break, which was one of her typical characteristics, shared with her brother. Mandargi was a hundred times better than all that!

Bright indolent sunshine streamed through the venetian blinds, leaving gold bars to balance the shadows. Great lazy butterflies drifted by the open window with sweet languor, velvety black against the blazing blue sky, and the air was heavy with the scent of unseen flowers crushed and bowed by the hail. It was compensation for life in the wilds, the brilliance and exotica; the wild gorges, the jungle, the lily-strewn lagoons, the jade-green blady grass that rose man-high; the remote river crossings where the crocodile basked in the sun, the shadowy thickets of tea-tree and bush wattle, the giant banyan trees; gardens full of crimson poincianas the yellow cascara trees, the heliotrope orchids, the brilliant parasite, the bougainvillea that climbed in such profusion everywhere. Even a tulip tree broke out its orange blossom outside the kitchen window. The Wet was a time of revival that set new life seething in the warm soil. And always the birds around them, the prolific wild life.

No wonder at all that men who lived so richly and urgently with elemental forces assumed a far different character from their city counterparts. They were tough, self-sufficient and superbly resourceful, at home in the remote, least visited places. Though no woman was expected to match them, for Paul's sake, Toni could put up a moderately capable performance. A vision of Damon Nyland filled her mind. She couldn't have ejected it, if a fortune depended upon it – the price of always thinking in pictures. Indeed it was difficult not to think of him without highly coloured pictures and phrases. Perhaps the hit on the head had undermined her resistance, inducing an "acute anxiety state" in up-to-date jargon. It was a not infrequent case, and here she was falling an easy

40

victim to cool, calculating charm, the concrete advantage that the man enjoyed over everyone.

She closed her dark eyes, heaving an exaggerated sigh of protest. Having him in the house was like waiting for another storm to burst. It took heart and imagination to combat that. A growing lassitude closed around her like a mist, leaving her temporarily without strength or resource. Oddly enough, she slept.

CHAPTER THREE

By the late afternoon she was aching with boredom, nearly mothered out of her skin by Tikka, bent on making amends for the previous day's shortcomings. From the end of the hallway came the wheezy chimes of the old grandfather clock. Somehow it brought everything to a head. She couldn't lie around any longer, the only way to resolve her dilemma was to get up. She moved slowly, a little stiffly, but fortunately seemed unaware of it. It took her a little longer than usual to get dressed, but the short buttercup yellow with its brief halter top was easy to get into and left her arms bare.

She paused for a moment before the sparkling mirror. She was pale, all eyes and obvious cheekbones and glowing hair. Always slender, it didn't seem possible she had lost weight overnight, but she was fairly certain she had. Perhaps a touch of lipstick would brighten up her appearance? She searched out a tube from the drawer and touched her mouth a glossy sand-rose, but it only drew attention to her pallor. With only half her mind given to the operation she blotted it nearly all off, leaving only a satiny suggestion of colour.

Outside in the hallway, the house was utterly still so that her own quickened breath seemed an intrusion. She moved along the passageway as silently as any shadow with the oddest notion that she was involved in some dangerous game. The very listening quality of the silence added to the delusion. A drift of rich scent wafted in from the garden; frangipanni, a cloud of honeysuckle and oleander. She lifted her head and her delicate nostrils flared. Something else – cigarette smoke, an expensive brand. A hot quick tingle ran down her spine. She wheeled about and looked into the study, her voice a little shaken.

"Who's there?"

"So the game's up!" A deep, mocking voice reached her and she was looking at the back of a well-shaped head, the intense blackness of thick hair. He swung around in the swivel chair and stood up in one lithe movement, an object lesson in tigerish grace, she thought, trying to project antagonism into what was, undeniably, a certain wry admiration. Across the space of the room the faint mockery dissolved into a swift look of intent. His face at that moment was a curious paradox, a mixture of cool arrogance and an overlay of a disarming gentleness.

"You're still pale!" he said, and smiled at her.

"Perhaps – but not, I think, in a state of collapse!"

"How's the head?" He reached back to the desk and slammed a report shut.

"Variable. Like a weather bulletin. It comes and goes. I'm not going back to bed, at any rate!"

He shrugged with that hard, baffling charm. "Do as you please! You're going to anyway. Is it really so necessary to set an example?"

"It's necessary not to go mad," she said feelingly, leaning against the door jamb, very young and slender. "About four o'clock I gave up. Nothing odd in that, really. I detest waiting around!"

"All life is waiting!" he said calmly with superficial tolerance. "You should know that. Waiting for this. waiting for that. Waiting for something, *someone*, to happen." His mouth twisted sardonically and he began to walk towards her. "In any case, I can't say it limps along here!"

Illogically Toni's eyes widened and her bones seemed to melt, realising his personal magnetism was strengthening by the minute. She'd better stop caring what he looked like or how he behaved or learn what compromise was. Her eyes searched beyond his wide shoulders to the windowless study, restored to some semblance of order.

"I'm lucky it wasn't worse!" she said with a throb of emotion.

43

"You are," he agreed dryly, "but let's not dwell on it! Now, if you're going to do the thing at all, you might as well do it properly. Come along like a good child, and I'll take you for a run around the property, get a breath of fresh air!"

"But this morning you said . . ."

He shifted his glance, studying her with maddening detachment. "Never mind what I said. That was this morning. In any case, you must make these charitable little gestures. I *am* the boss, after all."

"*Droit du seigneur*? Or you call the tune and we'll all dance!" She was leaning back, looking directly into his face, her body curving sideways on its narrow waist. His low spurt of laughter filled her with confusion, his glance so level and intent she couldn't break away from it.

"What a wicked, wild way of talking! I never implied that – you did!"

A glow brightened her dark eyes, contradicted by the assumed expression of sweet innocence that had worked very well in the past. "You're very tough, aren't you, Mr. Nyland?"

There was a gleam of pure malice in his green eyes and behind the malice unswerving attention. "*Firm*," he corrected. "I don't often deign to discuss it, but I am. Especially with women."

"And all I can do is stand around and agree!"

His glance glittered over her face, startlingly candid. He looked a little hard, arrogant eyes and mouth,

44

master of limitless horizons. "I think you ask questions for the perverse pleasure of being able to contradict!"

"It's possible." She bent her head and locked her hands together, surprised to find they were trembling slightly. "I'm sorry. I'm a nuisance, I know. Don't let me interfere with your plans." She turned and walked away from him, her slender back straight. He caught her up easily, his smile faintly cynical.

"Are you suggesting some way you can? Unexplored possibilities are always fascinating!"

Something odd and compelling stretched between them so that she had the terribly strong premonition that she must not touch him. Just talking to him was a kind of unabated excitement. He was a past master at this game, in fact, she was coming to realise he had a practised way, a sure knowledge of women. Her brain was telling her now what her senses had done. Her hand fell away abruptly from her temples with their sensitive modelling.

They walked from the deep cool haven of the veranda into the golden shower of late afternoon sunlight, an excess of illumination. Yellow gold trumpets of allamanda, droves of birds fluttering everywhere. The air was warm and sweet with the overpowering scent of tropical plants, the tangle of shrubbery starred with tiny white blossoms. He glanced down at her bright head, the heavy sweep of dark lashes that swept her cheek.

"What really brought you up here?" he asked crisply, straight to the point. "A thwarted love affair?"

There was an ironic slant to her feathery dark brows. "To my endless chagrin, I can't actually lay claim to a real love affair!"

His downbent glance was spiked with amusement.

"You ask me to believe that? Women, the attractive ones, are always in love, or not in love. Not a one of them's able to resist the compulsive urge to complicate their private lives!" His hand descended lightly on her shoulder as he steered her towards the parked station wagon. She felt the shock of it right through to her bones, but she wouldn't give in to the weakness of the sensation.

"As for me," she said hardily with a great deal more conviction than she was feeling, "I don't exactly know when that will be!"

"Then you can't see very far at all!"

"That's what's bothering me." She averted her face in a rather childlike gesture, moving ahead. Flowers were everywhere, strewn all about by the storm, bird song warm and full, and above all the sun, the tropic sun. Quickly she went to open the car door, but his hand beat hers to the gleaming chrome. "It's all right, I can manage," she said a little tersely, perturbed by his nearness – humiliating, but there it was, and no way to deny it.

His voice was faintly bantering. "Of course, you're all grown up, beset by the problems of equality. Why

46

don't you stop resisting and see what it's like?"

She didn't answer him but slid across the seat as fastidious as a cat. His cool glance moved lightly over her long legs, then he shut the door on her and came around to the driver's side of the vehicle. A man like that could play hell with a woman, she thought, every intuition grasping at the fact, but not *this* one. She had too much common sense for that!

In another second he was beside her, making a jumble of all her resolute notions. His glance slid over her, light and knowing, then he reached across to the glove box to extract the keys, fitted them into the ignition.

"I don't know what sort of job *you* did," he said sardonically, "but there you have one good reason why women are no good at the big jobs. Routine suits them better. They like plenty of scope for mooning about their love lives!"

She regarded him solemnly, all eyes, her mouth faintly parted with an unspoken protest that died on her lips. Swinging dark vitality. Rock-hard masculinity. Why wouldn't he talk like that? What else could she expect. Yet perversely these were the kind of men women were drawn to. It just didn't add up, like most things in life. The only weapon she had at her disposal was a slow, subtle smile that had worked very well in the past.

"Very cordially put, Mr. Nyland. I quite see that I for one lack the serious, responsible, objective approach of the male!"

"No doubt about it! And don't look at me like that, little one. I'm impervious to black eyes and long lashes, though I have to admit they're a nice combination!"

The amused patronage in his tone made her eyes sparkle, brought colour to her cheeks. "Well, that's cleared up a few things very neatly, if they even needed clarification. You're a woman-hater!"

He gave a low laugh and slid his arm along the seat, turning his dark head to reverse out of the shaded area. "Which just goes to prove my point," he stopped and changed gear, "*you're* showing a fine instinctive contempt for pure logic!"

Toni turned her head swiftly so that her hair fell forward in a rose-amber sweep. "The feminine instinct, Mr. Nyland," she said sweetly, "is at least twice as good as a man's training. If women were no good at all the human race would have scrapped them and started again!"

"Good God!" his smile was very white, quietly amused. "Who said they were no good? Why, in lots of ways, Miss Stewart, I think they're incomparable."

She made a decision in a split second, knowing she would never win with him. "Oh!" she said softly, disarmingly, her creamy face still. "I thought you were all set to criticise and criticise!"

"Why should I? You look as if you've had enough!" Something flickered in the clear depths of his eyes and he gave that white, very devastating grin.

"I know the older I get, the less I know about men!"

she said with some melodrama.

"There's always a sure cure, sunflower."

"Which is? I must know the truth."

"Give yourself a little time," he said lazily, "and you'll come to it all by yourself. Who knows, every last hope may be realised." His glance flickered over her and she shook her head as if warding him off, fairly caught by the devilry that flared in his eyes, that mysterious force that seemed to leap out at her.

"You're a strange man!" she said slowly, driven by some compulsion, her dark eyes touching each separate feature of his face.

"More complicated than you think!"

"Is that a warning?"

His voice was idly amused, his eyes mocking her. "My dear child, I never meant to imply any such thing." Sunlight struck obliquely across his dark copper skin, his eyes in the shadow jade green. They were moving in a swirl of dust down the bush track and she touched a hand to her throat, some weakness, part physical, moving over her, but she refused to give in to it.

"It doesn't mean anything to you, does it, scoring over women?"

"So now you know my secret! I wish I knew yours."

"I haven't got one!" she protested, over-quick.

"Oh yes, you have! We've all got one, and I've got inexhaustible patience. Now, enough of this nonsense. There's something I want you to do for me."

"I might have known!"

He turned his head swiftly, catching her unguarded glance. "That's how it is, little one. I'm not the big wheeler-dealer for nothing!"

"With terrible implications for myself, I feel sure."

His narrowing eyes lightly mocked her. "Such clear-sightedness! With luck, Miss Stewart, you'll go far!"

The gentle raillery piqued her, for it seemed it had a slight edge, an unnerving perceptiveness that saw inside her heart and head.

"The storm didn't do as much damage as I thought!" she said, not quite accurately, striving for a safe, fruitful topic.

He smiled, amused by the turn in the conversation, and she noticed again how the smile lit the sombre, rather imperious cast of his face. The miles of Mandargi flew by, fence and grassland, the grazing cattle, pure-bred Herefords for the most part. The frost-cool green eyes seemed focused on nothing in particular, yet he saw everything to right and left, strong hands on the wheel, relaxed yet alert like a steel spring.

"The property looks good," he said almost off-handedly. "When I first bought it, it had been allowed to run down. The former owner had lost all interest in it, wouldn't spend any money on improvements or even its upkeep."

"Perhaps he didn't *have* any! It does make a difference."

"He had it all right," he pointed out with the cool

emphasis of a man who knows his ground. "But he had some private problems he found hard to live with. His wife ran off with the first footloose adventurer to offer her a good time. At least she made it back to the city, and she was lucky to have made it at all. He was a very poor type, extracted a 'loan' from just about everyone for miles around."

"Not you?"

"A rhetorical question, I take it! No, not me, marigold. I don't listen to hard luck stories."

"I'll remember!"

"Courtesy will get you nowhere," he said dryly, "but to return to my story ... apparently the wife found the loneliness intolerable. No company, no taste at all for the wild and melancholy times."

"Yet it's so beautiful! A compensation, surely?"

He turned on her swiftly, in his eyes a mixture of irony and a deep cynicism. "You surprise me. I've collected a lot of significant data, and in the main, I've found women to be extraordinarily gregarious – community-minded. They want noise and chatter and lots of friends in, a life of cushioned ease. The better looking they are, the bigger the ideas. Gracious living at the very least. Who cares about the necessities, it's the luxuries that count! But for contentment, they all need a husband with a safe job, never mind if he likes it or not, a comfortable house and healthy kids. A woman's values!"

"Not *bad* ones, surely?"

"As far as they go. They won't admit it, but women set their own limits on their achievements. In a way they condemn themselves to a life of mediocrity, then they have the gall to blame men for it. They live for the here and now, not tomorrow. Even when they are trained to something big, they pull out at the last ditch and get married. Race off and have six kids!"

"Not *six*!" she said faintly. "Not these days!"

"No, they even set a limit on that particular accomplishment! We've lost all our pioneers."

For a moment her dark eyes, large and liquid, seemed to absorb her face. "How infamous and unchivalrous – and you needn't smile! It absolutely *proves* you have an ingrained prejudice against women. Like most men!" she finished off roundly.

"Dear me, dear me," he said, gravely mocking, insufferably high-handed and domineering. "A very shrewd hit, Miss Stewart. Twenty-two and a spinster! But I'm far too wise a fox to be baited, so don't use those velvety eyes to outwit me. I'm merely trying to point out that a man still builds for the future, and he doesn't mind roughing it, going without, for just as long as it takes."

"Have you roughed it, Mr. Nyland?" she asked sweetly, her eyes on his lean clever hands.

"I didn't always have what I've got now, honey tongue, and precious little help and encouragement." His green glance slipped over her with the degree of arrogance of a man who always got his way. "A word of advice, little one. Watch that tongue! It could scare the wits out of the local lads – something of a handicap in the matrimonial stakes. Still, they might be prepared to overlook it for the more exhilarating qualities. You're absurdly chic for the Outback. Your hair, what colour is it? A rose bronze? Very unusual with dark eyes and a camellia skin. I quite expected your brother's brilliant blue eyes duplicated. You must have enjoyed considerable success in the city. Swarming all over the place, like bees with wild honey!" He didn't think it necessary to add that *his* ear was caught by her voice, which was lovely, warm and vital. It came to him now, for a hundred reasons, trying to jar his composure.

"I thought you implied that they'd all run the other way! In fact, you sound as if all one could reasonably ask of a woman is that she be good-looking!"

He looked at her directly and she had a moment of devastating uncertainty. "I've known quite a few," he said dryly, "yet I'm always surprised when they say the right thing, always supposing they manage anything very much at all."

"When they endorse a few of *your* golden words, you mean!"

"Bitch!" he said gently, and laughed in his throat. "Opinionated women are never popular. Remember it, my impudent young friend!"

"So now you're disenchanted?" Her brilliant, youthful face confronted his dark, controlled one.

"Stone cold!" he said lightly. "In fact, I only want a son to carry on all I've built up, I'd never marry at all. Failures are so damned expensive."

"You're rather a case, aren't you?"

"Hard as nails!" His eyes met hers and her heart gave a great lurch. The eyes were completely baffling, as was everything about that contradictory man. The visionary: benevolent dictator, shrewd and calculating, the shattering, unsettling glimpses of near-tenderness.

"But very attractive!" she managed at last. Complete detachment of the impartial observer.

His smile fetched a white line in that darkly tanned skin. "So I've been told! But not nearly so attractive without my more concrete lasting assets. Savannah, for one. A man doesn't reach my age with many illusions intact about your sweetly unscrupulous sex. Avid little fingers, cased in velvet!"

Toni started to quote lightly, lowering her lashes over a malicious sparkle. "Give crowns and pounds and guineas, but not your heart away! And you won't give either!"

"Do you blame me? You know, little one, I like you. You even appear to be honest, but I've been tricked before – by brown eyes, as it happened!"

She drew a hand over her face as if she were brushing away cobwebs. "I don't relish my position then. Trying to prove myself at every turn just as though you'd washed your hands of all of us!"

"I certainly don't bear *you* a grudge," he remarked blandly, his eyes on her face. "In fact, I never rush into judgments. It's a dangerous habit!"

A pity about his smile, she thought, feeling hopelessly at a disadvantage. It hovered somewhere between mockery and a sensual element as strong as an electric current. She obeyed an irresistible impulse and smiled at him, using every bit of her not inconsiderable charm. But his firm mouth only relaxed into a grin. Top marks for effort. The glittery gaze slid over her half disparagingly.

"You must have been a ravishingly pretty child, but you've got too much to say for yourself!"

"You can't have it both ways!" She looked back at him, flippantly, unwilling to concede him a victory.

"Who says I can't!" he drawled with exquisite distinctness. "At this juncture, I've got it made!"

She was on the defensive now, excited, a little moody, perplexed by some odd shift in his manner. "This is an insane conversation!"

"Isn't it, and I've the feeling we're going to continue it every time we meet. You may be wild in your ways, but your face is beautiful. A very exotic butterfly!"

The sun struck across her eyes and she turned her head away. "I'd love to see Savannah," she announced in a politely enthusiastic voice.

"Now there's a cunning, opening wedge and no mistake! All right, then, you *will*, and sooner than you think, which is what I wanted to talk to you about.

55

Let's get out." He ran the car into the shade of a grove of low, shrubby trees, with light leaves and coarse bark, the aromatic sandalwoods. In another minute he had her out of the car, powerful, quiet and purposeful, with that disconcerting dash of diablerie, a light steely grip on her wrist.

"It has a sort of listening quietness, hasn't it?" she asked, over the swift, fiery beat of her heart.

He looked at her thoughtfully, seeing the pull of the place in her fine, dark eyes. "That's it, exactly. The particular spell of the tropics!" His gaze shifted to the distant line of the ranges, stretching for untold distances like a sea of blue-green; the rain forest, honeycombed with cliffs and ravines, wild creeks and gorges where waterfalls rushed and tumbled into rock pools. Vibrant, flutelike calls punctuated the stillness and a flock of corellas fluttered like flags overhead. Long massed grasses lay tossed by the storm, still glistening with moisture in the places not penetrated by the bush sunlight. The smell of the earth was good, the elusive tang of airborne flowers, with an underlying exquisite scent, almost like freesias, white-petalled and very sweet.

"Not so very long ago," he said quietly, "my father's day, this was the wild north – still is, in lots of respects. I grew up on tales of pearls and gold and tinfields; of clashes between white and black, bloody and to the death; land grabs and cattle duffing and herds of magnificent wild horses that made their kingdom in the

grasslands; tribal murders and black magic and crocodile shooters who went mad with the loneliness and isolation, the near-inaccessibility in the Wet. Plenty to
keep a small boy going. No wonder at all I had to come
back!" His gaze descended on her, delicately practised,
yet she saw clearly, a woman was no more than a piece
in a pattern to him. The land was his real life. "If it's
freedom you want, pretty bird," he said lightly, "then
you've got it. I know I feel hemmed in almost any
place else!"

She was looking back at him with an unconscious
air of expectancy. The breeze skeined her hair across
her face, silky and lucent, pointing up the flawless perfection of young, healthy skin. The sheen and the
shimmer, the one against the other. Dark ardent eyes.
The silence seemed infinite. It was impossible to break
that ice-green gaze. So much for her good intentions!
He was only trying to subjugate her with the force of
his personality – an easy task. The mighty male, and
she the second-class citizen. Power and arrogance, she
thought wryly. A great big do-as-I-please, that was
Damon Nyland with his lean, hard body and stark,
exciting face. His eyes were brilliant with life, clear
and glittery, mistakenly placed in a face far too dark
for them, an extraordinary contrast, startling to the
beholder. They narrowed suddenly, and the corners of
his firm mouth dented with amusement.

"What's on your mind?"

"Rebellion," she said.

His dark head came up like a thoroughbred and his aspect changed as if he had accepted the challenge. "For a moment there, I thought I'd committed every crime in the calendar. For some unknown, undeserved reason, you appear to have taken a firm dislike to me. A crushing blow!"

"Indeed I haven't!" she said with some irony.

"Women invariably betray themselves in a thousand small, eloquent ways! Yet your brother praises you to the skies – your beauty, your accomplishments, the sweetness of your disposition, charming and docile. I can only assume he's prejudiced. So far as I can judge, you've been pampered and spoiled out of all reason. The red hair makes it worse, of course."

A new wisdom told her to say nothing. She moved away from him quickly, with a unique elegance and no clear idea of where she was heading.

"You're full of a demon energy all of a sudden!" He was beside her, studying her with great interest like a museum piece under glass.

"I didn't want to be provoked into any unwonted admissions!" she said with some truth.

Instantly he dropped a restraining hand on her shoulder, laughing in his throat. "You won't *beat* me, little one, but if it seems any recompense, you stand a better chance than most of getting the odd hit home!" He glanced down at her bright head and his voice sharpened. "You're trembling slightly – what the devil!"

He gave the impression of great force and vigour

and she had to smile. "You've an unusually vivid personality, Mr. Nyland. Perhaps you were getting to me!"

"My *darling* child! Forgive me." He said it with the easy, careless charm of long practice. "Now how can I make amends? I know, we'll walk on a little way ahead. We Christians must share our treasures!"

Then they were walking across the untracked, mildly sloping part of the run, treading a thick, cushiony sea of bracken. The storm had brought up from the earth a sweet freshness that was extraordinarily restful. Ferns rose tall as a man with strong brown stems and bright green fronds outstretched like arms. He went on ahead, holding them before her face, the two of them united by the cool spell of the pre-sunset hour.

Ironwoods ringed them round, bush mahogany, chalky-barked poplar gums, the graceful tea-tree and acacia. Trees, so benign and beautiful, showing a new lushness with the approach of the Wet. Once a long, somnolent snake, curiously marked, slithered away from the man's foot, but he said nothing. His companion had missed it, as indeed, most would have, and besides, it was harmless. Bee-eaters swooped in low formation, the sun glancing off their blue-green body feathers, the coppery sheen of their heads.

They had gone about a quarter of a mile before they commenced the ascent of the sloping butt of the cliff face. The country was rougher, but they took it in easy stages. Stones dislodged by their shoes bounced away into the thick vegetation, but there were numerous anchors of saplings and ferns to cling to. Nearing the top, a spring spouted out, a silver fountain, marvellously picturesque, making a cool splashing sound.

"Storm water!" he said briefly, and turned to take her hand, drawing her up the rest of the slope. At the top, she stood beside him, bright head on a level with his shoulder, an apricot flush in her cheeks, panting slightly, pleasurably, from her exertions.

"Worth it?" He looked into her upflung face, then pointed to a strikingly semicircular entrance, framed by cool saplings in the freshest, palest shade of almond. It was a cave, and over the rock face drooped a long, lovely cascade of bush orchids; waxy cream into gold, speckled at the heart with magenta. A tumbling mass of blossom, a florist's dream, almost faultlessly arranged.

He reached up a long arm and plucked a flower, pushing it into her thick, silky hair with unerring fingers, surveying his handiwork with faintly sardonic eyes.

"Woman magic! It sizzles and burns! You're a pretty thing, young Toni, but let's go inside. Duck your head, like a good girl."

She bent almost double to enter the cave, but once inside she found there was plenty of room to stand upright. For a few moments it was almost impossible to distinguish anything after the brilliant sunshine, only a cool gloom, tinged with the lingering scent of herb smoke. The gloom merged into a soft, glimmering light.

"Why, it's marvellous!" she said in a young, entranced voice. "The perfect hidey-hole. Children would just love it!"

His brief laugh was indulgent and impatient at once. "Hidey-hole? God, you're closer to the schoolroom than I thought!"

She scarcely heard him, her eyes widening in awed amazement. "But this is a sacred place! On Mandargi."

"It is," he said rather dryly. "You're in the presence of the gift-bearers of the Dreamtime." He tilted her chin with one finger and she looked about her, her eyes circling the dim interior.

Around the walls and roof of the rock shelter glowed the good spirits of the Dreaming, mythical beings, some wearing ceremonial headdress, others with concentric circles for heads, surrounded by easily recognizable animals and trees, some abstract symbols, few, if any, understood. There was no sound, yet she heard spirit drums and tap-sticks and chanted prayers. A closed world of live magic, its psychic effect remarkable.

"Why, how perfect!" she said, her voice scarcely above a whisper as if she were in church. "And I never knew it was here!" She turned up her face to him, and her skin in the gloom had a visible, opalescent shimmer, her dark eyes wide.

"No one does, brown eyes," he said rather brusquely. "Only you and I know the secret, and the aborigines, of course. *I* only came on it by sheer chance and I'm insatiably curious. So here's your reward for being a good, uncomplaining child. Many a lesser woman would have taken to her bed for a week after your experience."

There was a smile in the depths of her eyes and she turned to him with slim, curving grace. "Why, thank you, Mr. Nyland. Sometimes you can be so unexpectedly nice!"

"Then's the time not to trust me!" he said abruptly, and began to laugh. "Well, have you seen enough? You've had enough adventure for one day. See you don't try to come here by yourself. It's way off the beaten track and you might get lost. Is that clear?"

Toni lifted her head, still caught in the magic net, anxious to please him, when from the deep, shallow recesses of the cave flapped a great, ugly bat, hardly moved from its pristine state, its inky black, membranous wings spread.

"Oh no!" She flung up her hands in an agony of fright and revulsion, not conscious of having walked or run or made any movement at all, but somehow she was locked within a hard protective circle of linked arms, her forehead pressed against the crisp, clean fragrance of his shirt. She hid her pale, incensed face with a little muffled exclamation.

"Don't panic!" he said above her head, his deep voice faintly mocking her. "Our friend just guards the place."

"Ugh!" Her slim shoulders shuddered involuntarily. "Hideous!"

"That's taken the shine out of things!"

"No, of course it hasn't! Really . . ." She lifted her head framed in the bright disarray of her hair, anxious to proclaim her true feelings, and as suddenly fell silent. Feathery waves of excitement mounted in her, beating about her like hidden wings. The whole of her melted into a look of complete femininity, willow-slender, and infinitely desirable.

"Don't do it!" he said, and the old mocking light was back in his eyes again with a new wariness.

"I don't understand!" She drew back from him, his dark face blurring under her eyes.

"You see how it could be, don't you?" His voice was hard, a shade reckless.

Her eyes sparkled like jet against the creamy pallor of her skin. It was impossible to mistake his meaning, excitement flaring like sheet lightning between them. "I feel shut in. Claustrophobic!" she said, speaking very rapidly.

"You can say that again!" There was a decided edge to his voice now and he seemed very tall and menacing, a complete stranger. Then his tone lightened. "Come along, flower face, you're obviously too young for it!" His fingers closed about her wrist, pulling her closer, holding her still. "You're perfectly safe with me!"

Why, he lived for domination. For mastery, she thought wildly. She was trembling slightly under the terrible toll of sexual attraction, fearing it a weakness.

"You'd like to see me grovel, wouldn't you?" she burst out, the soft, furious colour flooding her skin, adding to her look of abandonment.

"Why, you perverse little witch!" His eyes were no more than glittery slits, slashing at her. "You almost convince me!"

Then he was swinging her into his arms, kissing her, like no civilised man but a sorcerer, so that she was defenceless, without the power to resist, her mouth clinging, her body fluid and yielding, no thinking creature, but feeling ... *feeling* ... sheets of it, a burning, never-to-be-borne enchantment ... a magic circle of fire.

When his mouth left hers, she could have cried out. It was like being bereft, cut off from the life force. Electrifying pulses throbbed through her. Toni turned away blindly, so filled with new bewildering emotions that they overflowed in her. She had nothing to say.

His lean frame barred the entrance. He bent his dark head to her. "Why so frantic? I'd have thought you got kissed every other day!"

"Not like that!"

Now why had she admitted it, unless her self-control had gone racing over the moon?

"Then it's my turn to apologise, though you asked for it!" His manner was so sardonic, so assured, never sensual, so wildly at variance with the preceding shattering minutes, she found it hard to credit that she had experienced them at all. His green eyes mocked her, like some jungle cat's. Perhaps it was a form of black magic. Love potions. Anything. He was marvellously gifted to be able to turn it on and off like that. She was rather frightened of him. Perhaps he knew it and found it necessary, for his attitude relented, a resigned indifference to her emotional lack of growth. He turned and led the way out of the cave into the voluptuous beauty of a tropical sunset.

She sighed deeply, her eyes enormous, purplish black.

"Give everything its exact value," he said crisply. "That way you won't complicate life for yourself. It's all a question of psychology."

She stared at him, still trembling, and rubbed the false, sweet kiss from her mouth. "I've no head at all for serious things."

"Quite right! I knew we could follow this to a logical conclusion. Forgive me, Toni." He seemed to be amused, and it depressed her all the more.

"I don't know why you should find that important," she said a shade bitterly.

"I thought I told you, I want you to do something for me, but that can wait."

She stared back at him, hopelessly, then she started

to laugh, the little break in her voice less than controlled. He reacted at once.

"We'll go back – you're tired. That's a sign of fatigue if ever I've heard one!"

There was no help for it but to go back with him, suffer his strong arm for ever by her side. They covered the distance in silence, the very silence unnatural, accentuating her feeling of utter unreality. He was oddly untameable, this cruel cat-man with his almost mesmeric attraction, his slanting dark brows and saturnine expression, the strange leaping lights in his eyes.

On the western horizon all the magic in the world was harnessed. Great billowing clouds of crimson and rose and gold, shot with an unearthly radiance. The Great Earth Mother was all about them, joyous and vivid, surging with new life on the edge of the Wet. Cassias and acacias and bauhinias, heavy with blossom spilt colour all over the bushland. The song of the wind. The calls of homing birds as they flew into the lovely chain of waterholes.

With never a word, her young face slightly averted, Toni glanced everywhere but at the man beside her. A silent, insistent rhythm throbbed through her veins, but she couldn't put a name to it. It clamoured within her like an urgent ecstasy, faithfully reproduced by the flowering wilderness that was Mandargi.

CHAPTER FOUR

After dinner they sat out in the cool of the veranda, the night wind filtering through the verdant screen of vines. The vast and velvet sky was spangled with diamonds, flung almost haphazardly across the heavens, and over the tip of the banyan tree hung the Southern Cross.

Toni, sunk in the shadowy depths of a bamboo chair, seemed alien to the men's conversation. It revolved leisurely but purposefully about the affairs of the station, Mandargi, and on to the last word in advance methods – Savannah; experimentation, breeding, feeding, crops. Cattle-mad! Toni thought wryly. All their thoughts and energies were devoted to quadrupeds. Ice tinkled in squat tumblers, soothing to the touch and the senses.

She studied them thoughtfully; one with love and affection, a considerable degree of sisterly pride. The other with a frustrating jumble of emotions. Certainly not love, but perilously close to an obsession. Both men were handsome, intelligent, vital. One, super-assured, worldly, successful. Despot. The other, up-and-coming, ambitious but basically not all that tough. No Nyland. Both of them were dedicated men. They would never change. Indeed, they thought themselves perfect, or near enough as not to matter. It was their womenfolk who had to change. They were the ones who would like it or lump it, make the sacrifices.

Occasionally she leant forward to the low table to pick up her own tall, frosty glass, and the light fell in a pool over her burnished head, her simple sea-coloured dress, her face and throat rising above it almost translucent. She was pale, worn out by unaccustomed emotions. Dinner had been a success, though it had cost her an effort. One look at the vast, hot boiled mess of chicken Tikka had thoughtfully prepared in advance had been enough to make Toni give up all ideas of mere supervision. She had picked up the cooling saucepan there and then and thrust it at the astonished Tikka, who was struggling to interpret the Miss's seeming extravagance.

"Take it! Go on, take it! Take it away!" Toni still heard her own voice sailing around the kitchen. Tikka had smiled and nodded, bewildered but pleased, bearing her steaming burden to the uncomplaining Albert, who eventually tucked it away. In spite of these handicaps, the urge to present a decent meal was strong in Toni. She cared about good food, from its preparation to its presentation, and she knew quite a bit about it, or liked to think she did. At any rate no one complained. The compliments flowed from the men over dinner, free and unfeigned, and she brushed them aside with a small smile. All in a day's work.

In the end they had rather an interesting appetiser

in the form of Gulf prawns with a tangy sauce and garnished with lemon. Steak, because time was short, but good Mandargi beef, crisp on the outside, faintly pink on the inside, juicy and tender and thick, served with a tossed salad, and afterwards, strawberry crêpes with cream and ice-cream, for no other reason than she was a rare hand with crêpes and the big turquoise strawberry pot had been brought into the shelter of the veranda while the fruit was ripening, thus saving it from the birds and, better still, the storm. Coffee, black and strong. Cheese if the men wanted it – they did. The two girls, very quick and neat in freshly laundered uniforms, waited at table, their merry black eyes bright with a delicate delight. It was a great treat to serve the Big Boss, who responded admirably, white teeth flashing in his dark, handsome face.

It was an effort, Toni reasoned, but well worth it. Mandargi's reputation had been sustained. It was a fantastic luxury to sit in the cool of the veranda, the familiar night sounds around them; laughter and shouts, the odd restrained swear word, a card game in progress over at the stockmen's quarters. The persistent warbling of a night-bird. Soft crooning aboriginal voices not altogether with a current pop record on the old gramophone. They had to speak to her twice before she heard them, then she turned to her brother with a faint start.

"I'm sorry, darling, I was listening to the recording. Tom Jones, isn't it?"

"Hardly. He'd get over that din. I'm sorry I ever gave them that old piece of junk — they never let up. I'd like to know where they get all the new records from."

"Buy them, of course. With their wages. Mack used to order them in. *Chacun à son gout*, you know!"

"Yes, indeed!" Nyland supplied suavely, as though asked his opinion. "I like women with a touch of vinegar. Lends a flavour!"

Paul looked at him with mild surprise, then laughed. He *had* been aware of the cross-currents during dinner. "Mr. Nyland . . ." he began.

"Damon!" Nyland corrected with some charm and right at the precise, psychological moment.

"*Damon*," Paul saluted the older man with his glass and a lazy smile . . . "wants to beg a certain favour."

"I've been trying to get around to it all day." Nyland picked up the cue neatly. "The fact is, Toni, there is a way you can help me if you would." His green eyes watched her with a challenging stare. An "I-know-you-damn-well-dislike-me, but say-it-if-you-dare" look.

She met his gaze readily enough, her face slightly frozen, and he smiled.

"Encouragement is what I want! I do wish you'd try to hear me out, little one!"

"Of course!" she said, as outspoken as ever.

"Thanks." He tipped back in his chair and the light fell across his face and she wished it hadn't. "I'll try to be brief. A woman relative of mine is coming to stay with me. In the nature of a rest cure. Peace and quiet, that sort of thing. She's had rather a bad time of it, but she's been very brave with that screwed-up kind of courage some women have. Her husband, a cousin of mine, was killed in a car crash about eighteen months ago. It was all very tragic. He was only thirty-one, leaving Elissa and one child – a small girl, Anne or Annette, I'm not sure. I gather she's something of a handful and Lissa's not strong. Fragile, I suppose you'd say."

"And where do I come in?" Toni asked faintly, but straight from the heart. A fragile, introverted mother? A difficult child?

"I think your company," he said with careless grandeur, "would do Elissa the world of good. She's become very withdrawn. Bad at her age, and whatever else you are, Toni, you're bright company. It would only be for a week or so. My solicitors are handling the hiring of a governess for the child, but it will be some time before she arrives. In the meantime I don't want Elissa to be on her own. I know she'd be glad of another woman's company and the child is too much for her. Missing the man's hand, I suppose."

We *all* are! Toni thought wryly, at once and for ever on Annette's side. The initial shock had worn off. He might crack the whip for miles around, but she

71

had other ideas. "Please, Mr. Nyland," she said lightly, her dark eyes sparkling, "you're asking for the moon! Mandargi needs me. Paul needs me. Paul?" She turned her high-spirited face to her brother for confirmation, but he was studying the level of the whisky bottle with the complete absorption of an alcoholic. Diplomacy was one of his great assets.

Nyland, in turn, looked back at her with the cool self-containment of a statue cast in bronze. "Paul," he said suavely, "has been good enough to suggest that he can struggle along for a fortnight, but rather than let him do that, I'll send over one of my own staff to handle the cooking arrangements. He won't starve, never fear. Neither will the men. Mrs. Carroll mightn't approach your excellence, but she's what is known as a good, plain cook and she's very strong. She'll cope, not to speak of managing the girls. I think you'll find she'll perform some small miracles there!"

She stared back at him as if they had just exchanged insults. Nothing in her life had ever prepared her for such cool insolence. The trouble was, she dreaded domination, and he had a remarkable talent for riding roughshod over all opposition.

"Bullied and beaten!" she said frankly, speaking her thoughts aloud. "I wonder you think of me, Mr. Nyland. Surely there's someone else you'd much rather ask?"

"Absolutely not! The truth is, I knew it the moment I laid eyes on you." His eyes touched her face,

72

effortlessly able to fascinate. "You will do it, Toni? Help me out. It's all in a good cause, and you're such a good-hearted little thing. Paul's been telling me!" There was a hard, mocking glint in his eyes that suggested that he really thought her an unruly brat with reckless impulses but was too polite, or too cunning, or both, to mention it.

She was very still, her slender body tilted from the waist, looking out over the star-spangled night. "In that case, Mr. Nyland," she said with a touch of his own superb irony, "I'd be pleased to. Shall we drink to it?"

"You're very kind!" His dark-timbred voice dropped to an intimate undertone. "You've no idea what it means to me!"

"None whatsoever!" she said with a swift return to her old pugnacious self, thinking it a very poor show how Paul had deserted her like that. Her idea of Mandargi as a refuge was no more than a rose-coloured fantasy. This invitation, this *summons*, to Savannah, was symbolic, a demonstration of authority.

"I'll pay you, of course, so you won't think it's charity!" he said, gleaming eyes shadowed with some knowledge she found unbearably exciting. And she was being sent into enforced daily encounter with him! He continued to study her, very experienced, very cynical, very sure of what he wanted in a woman, a twist to his mobile, provocative mouth.

"You beast!" She withdrew to the safety of the shellbacked chair, her dark eyes melancholy, admitting her vulnerability and not caring.

"Always when I discuss money." He reached over lazily and tipped a little ginger ale into her glass. "Here, let me top up your drink." His eyes flicked her face briefly, daring her to speak again. Toni had this wild, irrational impulse to flail her fists at him, hammer him with puny blows. Acting in her interests? However could she believe in such a myth? She fell silent. Out-witted, out-manoeuvred, manipulated, probably to play gooseberry on Savannah. Ashamed of herself, she cancelled out that last idea. What had come over her? Some weird personality change? The woman was a widow, only recently bereaved. A small child missing her father, needing an emotional outlet. She was ashamed of herself. She would go to Savannah and give of her very best and she wouldn't accept a penny for it. She would make sure of that. Damon Nyland had a woman of consequence and character to reckon with.

Apparently it didn't bother him unduly, for he was already fathoms deep in conversation with Paul again. In another minute she would excuse herself for the night. They would never miss her, in any case. Probably they wouldn't even hear her say goodnight! Words impinged on her ear, making her change her mind. A dawn mustering! To ride out in the cool, mother-of-pearl light. Coffee round the camp fire, a circle of tanned faces. The flame of dawn in the sky. Very early sunlight, pale as honey. Tree shadows. Hooves stamping, impatient to be off.

"Can I come?" The words flew out, in brilliant animation, heightened by a rare susceptibility.

"No!" Nyland said very calmly. "You'll only get into trouble. Women and cattle don't mix. Besides, you have to watch your arm."

"My arm doesn't bother me in the least!" she said rather emotionally.

"You'd be the last to admit it if it did!"

"It's pretty rough work, honey," Paul broke into the conversation, his eyes on his sister's vivid young face, the lustrous sheen in her eyes. "You haven't seen too much at all as far as that goes. We'll be mustering, separating, branding, that sort of thing. A welter of noise and confusion. You've heard the calves bellow, and there's danger too. It gets terribly hot as the day wears on, and the dust and everything..." He knew, from experience, he was fighting a losing battle. Toni had a trick of getting her own way, especially with *him*. Many was the guilty moment he had endured on her behalf, leaving her to Myra's tender mercies when she was little more than a child with thick, glossy pigtails and never a sign of reproach in those great dark eyes.

Nyland, looking at his face, knew the younger man was weakening. A mistake with young things that needed gentling but plenty of control. It was easy to recognise his opposition, for he had dropped all pretence, his autocratic dark face set in lines that suggested argument would be useless, much less a private feud.

"I know I'm going to love it!" Toni found herself saying. "Ordinary riding clothes be all right?"

"Drop it, little one, while you're in front," Nyland said easily, with only a token attempt at placation.

"Another time, perhaps, when you're more used to our way of life and you haven't had a hit on the head. It's hard riding and you're unaccustomed to it. You wouldn't stay the distance and you'd have to ride back by yourself in the heat." He paused for a moment and his eyes seemed to change subtly. They were cooler, clearer, very frank. A half smile hovered near his mouth. "You go right ahead and go to bed. You look tired and tense. We'll just take our time." He said it as if he had spent a lifetime considering her wellbeing.

Oh, he was clever! A clever, dangerous, urbanely affable antagonist. She had known it all the time. "Do you know it's the *oddest* thing!" she said almost incredulously, then broke off, conscious she was talking like a woman in a melodrama. She wanted to be alone, more than anything in the world. "Really, I intend to go," she said quietly, firmly, no silly girl-child. "That's my final word!"

"Why, that sounds fascinating!" Nyland gave a low laugh and from the look on his face he meant it.

"Mutiny?"

"Oh no! Give up, kiddo. Looks like you're defeated on this one!" Paul said in his charming drawl, thinking it not all that important.

"How very friendly of you!" Toni said sweetly. *Give up?* she'd show them! They had no right to discriminate against her. With a jolt she realised she was on the verge of losing her temper. That would never do. She had to save her energies. In any case, she simply didn't care enough to feel insulted. She surveyed them bright-eyed, spreading her hands in an appealing little gesture. "Forgive me, I *am* a little tired. I'll say good night."

Their faces relaxed, softened. They came to their feet, smiling, as though they found her enormously engaging. In the half-light, half-shadow, they looked exaggeratedly tall, powerful, graceful too. Wide in the shoulders, lean in the hips. Cattle men, to be treated with caution. Good friends and neighbours. Nyland sketched an elegant little salute and she felt a surge of murderous rage that carried her in a fine blaze to her room. With any luck at all she would beat them out on to the track!

The moon was still in the sky when she got up, a silver sickle. She was happy, exhilarated, keyed up like a child about to start out on an unauthorised adventure. The pre-dawn wind was cool and moist, stroking her skin and making her hair curl. It fanned out the cur-

77

tains and made her whisper to herself: This is the best time of all!

She dressed swiftly, her movements keeping pace with her quickening pulse. Presently she was ready — riding pants, glistening riding boots, pale cotton shirt, spotted silk scarf to protect her nape and later on, her face, against the dust, a rakish gaucho hat, wide-brimmed and silver-strapped. She felt wide awake, diamond-bright, able to beat the opposition. It was an extra luxury to be able to sip at a cup of still scalding black coffee poured from the stainless steel thermos she had smuggled into her room the night before. Such foresight! She finished it up, then put the cup down, turning to smile at herself in the mirror with great affection. Everything was going to plan. She had even beaten the birds up!

It was impossibly risky to go back through the house. The window was the answer. It was only a short drop to the ground. In a flash she was through, landing lightly on the thick, springy grass. It was a magical morning, pearl grey, mystical, like being re-born. No shafts of opal light yet invaded the sky, no hordes of birds. Only the sweet, penetrating scent of some tiny white flowers she had crushed underfoot. Her first thought was to get to her horse — no quiet little working horse, but a sweet-tempered mare descended from the Arab. Toni rode well, correctly, taught as a child. Not as the hands on the station, born in the saddle, centaurs, part-man, part-horse, or they certainly gave that impression. Experts indeed, but she had nothing to be ashamed of.

She moved warily, always looking behind her, with any number of dodges, her heart hammering, as if she was on some guilty mission. She cut through the screen of the trees, head down, until she came out on the pebbled track that led to the stables. Suddenly, like some mysterious sun-signal, a great frieze of birds came flying up through the first flush of light, rising from the lagoon, straightening out their V formation, gliding in line. Shell parrots, hundreds of tiny green birds, the orange and crimson chats, unwinding like some multi-coloured bolt of silk across the sky.

Toni lifted her face, vivid with pleasure, melting dark eyes, filled with an intense love for this wild, fresh land, this paradise of tiny, chattering birds that seemed to ring her round, a shining massed escort. Up, up, up! A soft, swishing sound of wings, like the dawn breeze. She held up a hand, very young, very slender, with a dangerous vulnerability, an acute sensitivity that deepened her capacity for pleasure and pain.

Intent as she was on the birds' antics, it was doubly shocking to be caught up in one smooth, unhurried lunge, held in a sprung-steel trap. Off guard: she thought, her heart flipping in fright. Off guard. *As always*. Struck into an awed silence.

"You've heard about bushcraft, I take it," he said with great distinctness his eyes on her defenceless face. "Invaluable, I've found. Some sixth sense that always leads the hunter to the quarry. He knows exactly which path to take, which track to follow. He almost sees into the mind!"

"How clever!" she said dismally, wise enough not to struggle, feeling the first fright of reaction.

"You've changed your mind from last evening, I gather."

"Yes, but surely I have a good reason?" She tried to ignore the sarcasm, her dark eyes searching his face, wide and alarmed. How could she ever have imagined he would never guess her secret? He was alertly on guard, his supreme self-assurance never to be shaken.

He pulled at a short bright curl and wound it around his finger. "You're practically begging for it, aren't you? You don't think you fooled me with that little girl act last night? I saw the fine blaze in your eyes. A terrible weapon!"

Some deep running physical attraction was threatening to engulf her. She leaned back against his arm, her heart knocking against her ribs, seeing the gleam in his eyes and misliking their expression.

"I'm going! Yes, I am," she said intensely. "If you don't let me, I won't help you with your cousin, and you can't make me, so there!"

"Blackmail?" He seemed poised like a hawk, a sensual twist to his mouth.

"Something like that!" she said in a terse undertone. "If you can't lick 'em, join 'em!"

80

"Nothing doing!" He dropped his hands pointedly, never more heartless.

"Damon!" It was almost a cry from the heart, completely unpremeditated, and she could have bitten her tongue out.

"*Mr. Nyland* to you, brat!" He turned, his green eyes sweeping over her sensually alive.

"Mr. Nyland!" she corrected herself, and drew a deep, shuddering breath.

Inexplicably amusement leapt in his eyes. "Don't look so desperate!" He moved slowly back to her. "I was only fooling. Damon will do. It sounds altogether different the way you say it!"

Her hat hung down her back and her bare head glinted like the rise and fall of fire. Deliberately she pitched her voice to a bell tone, her feelings showing very plainly in her face. "Please let me come. I won't get in the way. You can trust me not to panic or lose my head. I've got the right hat on and I'll come back as soon as I've had enough. I'll even . . ."

". . . if you'll allow me to get a word in edgeways," he said quite pleasantly, for him, so that she stood rapt and still staring into his dark face, her soft mouth faintly parted. "You're very polite, very persuasive all of a sudden. I shouldn't be so surprised!" His lids came down, masking the brilliance of his eyes. "You agree to come to Savannah?"

"I do. One good deed deserves another!"

He gave a short laugh, not without humour. "Yes,

and I can see the effort it's taking! All right, then, *come*. Probably we'll both live to regret it, but I can't help myself. I'd have to be a wooden Indian to ignore your assets, and that's the proof!"

"Sarcasm before the sun's up, Mr. Nyland?" she asked him, and smiled, holding out her hand with a sudden impulsive motion.

"The simple truth, ma'am." He took her hand briefly, sounding brisk and factual, the hard arrogance back on him, then he spun on his heel. "Well, are you coming? Or determined to waste time? I can't pretend *I'm* doing the right thing!"

How like a man never to give in gracefully. "Oh, don't turn your back," she burst out impulsively. "Please look at me!"

"I know better!" he said briefly, charging ahead. "Excessive bravery is beyond me!" He was burning up the ground, moving lithely, with long, lengthy paces, aloof, self-contained, so that she had to run to keep up with him. Nearing the stables, he stopped so abruptly that she almost slammed into him. He caught her by the shoulders, lowering his dark head. "Now listen to me, flower face. I don't care how seductive you are. *Behave*. Do exactly what you're told today. Got it? *Exactly*, or there'll be hell to pay!"

Colour flooded her face, adding lustre to her eyes. The urge to tilt his authority was moving inexorably in her. "Yes, of course, Mr. Nyland. I do beg your pardon. Is there anything more you care to say?"

"That's it. That's the end!"

"That's enough!" Toni said with a helpless little cry. "You're hurting me!"

He drew back from her instantly, a disturbing element in his soft drawl. "I'm sorry, but you will stand so close to danger!" His eyes in the green gloom mocked her, his mouth twisted sardonically.

"I *believe* you!" she said, equally soft, never in her life one to think twice.

"I suppose you know you're going to get directly in the line of fire?"

"Am I?" she asked rashly, adding to her attractiveness.

He took a quick step towards her and her eyes went enormous. Whatever course of action he had in mind he obviously thought better of it. "Never mind!" he said with a hard, mocking grin. "We can always pick up the pieces later. Come along, velvet eyes, so sweet and simple and demure, I *don't* think!"

She thrust her hat on her soft fall of hair, tilting it to a dashing angle as a matter of course. Now perversely she wanted to please him. Was there any working it out? "Please don't let's quarrel and spoil things," she said, twisting to look into his dark face. "I'm a pacifist by nature!"

He laughed outright. "You're extremely clever and *very* disrespectful, but I suppose a girl can't have everything! Now, once and for all, come quietly and don't dance round me like a five-year-old or I might change my mind."

She slanted a glance at his straight profile – a good profile. His expression as usual, baffling, a faint curve of self-mockery to his shapely mouth. All at once she wanted to touch him, so badly she dared not think about it. What a fool, ruled by her emotions! She didn't even know him, so why this sense of affinity as if she'd known him in some other lifetime? A shower of excitement was tightening inside her like a closed fist. Damon spun his head as if she had thrown something at him, pinning her gaze. For a stricken minute she felt herself transparent. Every thought, every desire, everything she had ever felt, there for him to register.

"Well, well, well!" he said softly, in such a way and in such a voice that she turned and ran from him as if he were the devil himself.

CHAPTER FIVE

Cattle – rivers of them, great thundering torrents, that ran from everywhere. Joining up, jam-packed so you could have walked across their backs to almost anywhere. A big muster, thousands of head, a surging, living sea of liver and white hides, white faces, pink-rimmed eyes. Close-packed, churning hooves that sent dense cloud castles spiralling to the skies. The bellowing was frightful, bouncing off the eardrums, to live on for hours after all noise had ceased.

Every hand on the station had been called into action, black and white. Scarves, folded triangular fashion, were across their faces, some protection from the all-pervading dust. They swung in the saddle with an easy slouch, appearing to hardly touch the reins, the work horses trained to the point where they needed little direction to flank and press back the surging, solid walls of flesh.

The sun was up, full up, burning with great brilliance and power through the successive layers of red dust that fell back from the skies. Toni, in a near-frenzy of heat and strange sights, sat on the white fence at the cattleyards, her boots hooked through one of the lower rungs. Perched up beside her was Albert, the aboriginal stockboy — commentator, bodyguard. Both of them, like the men, wore their scarves tied under their eyes, but the dust was everywhere like an insidious fog.

Dust, daring, danger, Toni thought, soaking it in. Men who moved with seeming indifference and expert precision through all three. Calves separated from their mothers were frantic with fear. Anti-human. Woman-like, their agonised bellowing upset her. Roped, tied, branded. The sudden stench of singed hair and burnt flesh. The branding was not cruelly excessive but hard enough to leave a clear imprint of the stylised M. Ear-clipping, dehorning, castrating — but

Toni didn't watch that. Not in any circumstances. Enough was enough, she thought, her small nose wrinkling. She was swallowing constantly, convulsively — often, determined to learn something and not fall off the fence in sheer horrified revolt. At the very least, she learnt she was no cattle woman. Not the *first* time, perhaps never, though the whole spectacle had a savage, barbaric splendour; the aboriginal boys performing some weird ballet as they danced before hostile horns.

In the centre of the arena of noise and heat and confusion stood Paul with the Big Boss by his side. Their deeply tanned faces were almost obscured by their scarves and wide-brimmed Stetsons, their eyes narrowed against the glare and the grime. They were locked in an all-male world of decision and danger, on all sides protesting beasts with their great muscle power.

It was strange, utterly strange, quite unreal. The sun was slamming right into the small of her back.

"All right, Miss Toni?" Albert's voice came at a soft muffle through his bandana. "You're not askin' no questions no more!"

Under her scarf she gave a fixed little smile that tautened the silk across the bridge of her nose. She'd had enough, definitely enough. The question was, how was she going to be able to admit it and not lose face? As it happened, help came from an unexpected quarter. One of the hands in charge of the barbecue suddenly got hold of the old dinner gong and hit it with such force that it nearly stopped the charging cattle in their tracks, reverberating above the general yelling and bawling and pounding hooves.

To Toni, it was the ultimate act of aggression. It was her saviour too, for almost immediately Paul came over to her, pulling off his scarf from his dust-grimed face and wiping it carelessly.

"All right, kiddo? You look a bit green around the gills!"

A *bit* green? She eased off her own scarf, trying to appear jaunty and confident and never for one moment succeeding. "Perfect!" she said lightly, lying for all she was worth.

"You will be when you've had your lunch," Paul said comfortingly, assessing her with a doubtful eye. As it was, she had stuck it out far longer than he thought. He was proud of her. He turned to wink at Albert who had jumped off the fence, dead keen to obey the gong. "Did the Missy ask many questions?"

"Sure did, Boss!" Albert's face split into a grin. "At the jump, at any rate. Don't think she made much of the answers, eh, miss?"

"You were a great help to me, Albert," Toni said carefully, spacing her words carefully. "I think you could safely call it a profound experience!"

Albert let that one sail over his head. He made off with a grin and a backward wave of his hand. Now for the worst! In a half-fearful agony, Toni watched

87

Nyland's approach, bracing herself like some sapling to resist the storm. Even at a distance he had tremendous natural authority – alert, hard, all flowing muscle, possessor of a dark frightening energy that made her feel positively lifeless.

Within a few seconds those strange light eyes were turned on her full battery, studying each separate feature of her face, her undeniable sick tinge for all the apricot sun-spots.

"That spirited little air of yours is sadly out of evidence," he said crisply. "How do you feel?"

She gave a funny little quirk of her mouth, not daring to open it, lest the ground come up and hit her in the face. She had wished it all on herself. She had no one else to blame for her present dilemma, though she might wish she had. How he would *crow*!

Watching the expressions chase across her face, he suddenly reached up with barely controlled impatience lifted her clear of the fence, holding her lightly until she had regained her balance. "Perhaps you're looking in the wrong direction for a bit of excitement," he said, his voice terse, overlaid with a degree of – anxiety? It couldn't be. He kept his hand on her shoulder, pacing her gently towards the shade. "Are you hungry?"

"No!"

"Stay cool, sweetie, and you'll emerge triumphant!" Paul promised her, loping along easily beside them, his eyes very bright and observant, going from one to the other. "Never let it be said Toni Stewart sets her sights too high! It *is* a damned cruel, messy business to a woman. I suppose," he conceded with utter fairness.

"Please!" she held up a restraining hand, then pushed off her hat. Her hair slid forward in a gleaming arc, drawing the sun, flashing out highlights.

They walked into the broad pocket of green under the coolibahs. A wide, deep cavern, an oasis of peace and calm. Toni's mouth felt dry, the muscles of her throat almost locked rigid. She lifted a pale hand to her cheek. It was burning hot. The heat, that was it! She had been a long time in the saddle before that little lot. She needn't think too badly of herself.

The men smiled and tipped their hats respectfully. Some of them had already taken up positions on the ground, not even bothering to seek the shelter of the shade, gazing with great gusto at their heaped-up plates. Others were milling about wordlessly around the long trestle that had been set up a little distance from the barbecue, pouring various condiments over their charcoaled steaks, picking up great hunks of crusty newly baked bread; the lot to be washed down with lashings of billy tea before they were back on the job again until it was finished, and never mind the time!

Left alone for a few moments, Toni leant against the trunk of a tree. She tipped her head back, feeling strangely lightheaded. She was enormously grateful for the faintest zephyr of breeze that stirred the fine hair at her temples, for a cold dew seemed to be gathering across her forehead.

"Here, lovie, try this. It'll make a new woman of you!" Paul came back to her, appallingly fit and healthy, hungry as a hunter, but women and children first. He thrust a great steak at her, liberally doused in the tomato sauce she loathed. Toni opened her eyes to thank him, the smell of the food overpowering and extraordinarily distasteful, desperate to prove herself equal to it all, when the trees seemed to tilt then make a great leafy swoop for her.

She gave a small, frightened moan and found the only way possible out of her contretemps short of being violently ill. She fainted.

When she opened her eyes she was lying on the grass, some sort of blanket under her head.

"God, love!" Paul was staring into her face in the most peculiar fashion as if he had just been presented with a living truth: Women really were the weaker sex! Above him, dark and inexpressibly forbidding, stood Nyland, a quick lick of flame from his eyes: I-told-you-so!

Toni touched the tip of her tongue to her mouth, her eyes huge and distressed. Without a word Nyland dropped to his knees beside her, his face a teak mask. "Get some water from one of the canteens, Paul!" he said in a taut, clipped voice.

"I'm all right," she said huskily, into the shocked
90

silence, as if they none of them had seen such a thing.

"Like sweet hell you are!" he said vibrantly. "Someone will have to restrain your adventurous urges!"

"It was the steak. The food, the tomato sauce or something," she said fretfully, trying to absolve herself. "The unseen factor. It gets you every time. I'd have been all right but for that."

Paul came back at a run with a tin mug full of cold water. Nyland took it from him, got a hand to the back of her head and held the mug up to her mouth.

It had the *funniest* taste!

"Was that water?" she croaked.

Paul made an about-face, thunderstruck. "God knows! You've even got me befuddled. Yes, of course it was water. Wasn't it, Ed?"

Ed, the leading hand, took a quick swig of his water canteen, just to make sure. "Sure isn't brandy, Boss!"

Nyland's downbent gaze was comprehensive, frankly accusing. To bring a woman along on such a session was to invite a farce. He needed his head read!

"Well, I tried," she said with a faint return of spirit. "And I think I learnt a lot. We can't all belong to the master race!"

"No, indeed!" Nyland retorted very smartly. "But never mind, your motives are excellent, Toni, it's your judgement that's bad! I had the certain feeling all morning that something unusual was going to happen."

"Her colour is coming back, at any rate," Paul murmured, sounding faintly unnerved. He looked over his shoulder to where his leading hand was hovering. "Ed, run Miss Toni back to the house like a good chap. Take the ute."

"I'll take her back," Nyland said in a voice that settled all opposition. "I was fool enough to say she could come in the first place."

"As you like! It's very good of you, Damon." Paul straightened, tucking his shirt into his lithe waistline. "Well, what a funny old time you've had, kiddo. I always said your impulsiveness would get you into trouble!"

So they were closing their ranks on her! A fascinating insight into the male mind. "I'll go back by myself," she said hardily. "Believe me, I'm able to do just that!"

"Lady, we'll never believe you again!" His hands hard and steely, Nyland helped her to her feet, a wholly masculine look of superiority on his dark face. "Learn to give in gracefully, if nothing else. You're coming with me!"

"Yes, Mr. Nyland," she said respectfully, conscious all at once of the sea of interested faces.

"Right-oh, boys, back to work!" Paul spun on his heel, a suggestion of roughness in his voice. "It's not as if you can hang around till it suits you. I just hope none of you missed a bunch!"

Rather sheepishly the men choked down what was left on their plates and took themselves off, no doubt to discuss the whole thing at a later date. Toni had long discovered, contrary to the popular myth, that men *did* have their own private gossip sessions. A multitude of expressions played across her small face. Nyland looked across at her silently, some dark emotion too violent to be analysed in his own face. One thing was certain, he was fed up. Her eyes met his for a split second. His were frosty, faintly hostile, bright with this emotion that could have been anything. Most certainly indignation was thrown in.

She took a few compulsive steps forward, moving into a segment of light, her hair a glowing dark flame.

"Are you coming?" she asked over her shoulder, an imperious lilt to her voice.

His mouth thinned and his eyes glittered. He caught up with her, taking her elbow in a light, inflexible grip, dropping his voice to a mere thread of sound. "Whoever said mastery was primarily a masculine trait? It isn't, you know. Ever heard of a henpecked husband? God, you should have! There are enough of them. Peace at any price, but not me. No one, and I mean *no one*, speaks to me like that!"

"I'm sorry. I'm sorry!" she said over and over again, undergoing a curious transformation. "We'll never get on, will we?" she said mournfully. "Truth *is* stranger than fiction. We're two of a kind — pig-headed. Shared identities are always electrifying, but I couldn't bear to struggle to maintain my independence!"

They were almost at the utility and he stopped dead, listening to her half-incoherent muttering. As on a previous occasion when she had least expected it, he burst out laughing with the true ring of amusement — a lightning change.

"Look, little one," he said, sobering abruptly, "any relationship between a man and a woman is pretty fragile at the best of times. The thing is, do you want to get on with me? If you do, you have to work at it. I can't, or won't, I'm not sure which. For some unknown and quite unexpected reason, I happen to care what happens to you. You've got under my guard with all that nonsense you talk. Stirred up some sort of protective instinct I didn't know I had!"

For a moment she stared up at him, a gauzy moth infatuated with a flame. "Is that why you resent me, because you don't want to? Tell me!"

"I'm sorry. I simply can't. I suppose I do resent you in a way. We'll have to see a psychiatrist about it some time, but for the here and now, let's leave it. I came to Mandargi on a purely neighbourly action, not because I happen to own it. Now look what I've found. It almost persuades me never to lift a finger to help anyone again!"

It was his way to be flippant, to taunt her. She knew this, because it was her own way, yet she felt crushed, her breath uneven as if she were in dreadful pain. A queer little sob tore at her throat.

"Why, you little ass!" Damon's fingers dug into her curls, tightening over the nape of her neck. "Don't be so damned ridiculous. Don't you dare cry. I'd hate that!"

"How worrying for you! Don't be alarmed – I won't cry. I'm beyond tears!"

"Good!" He put her into the ute, flicking her one piercing glance before losing interest in her.

Her look of helpless femininity, had she known it, was ravishing, the glitter of tears in her wide-spaced dark eyes, the faint tremor in her curvy young mouth. In many ways he was a damnable man, she thought, relaxing her back against the seat and feeling a kind of exquisite, exhausted sweetness steal over her.

He kept the vehicle moving very fast, bent on not wasting too much of his precious time. His profile was without expression, remote even, for all its splendid dark arrogance. Toni drew in a long breath and released it shakily. His hard, masculine mouth curled slightly at the corners in a faint expression of amusement. His brief, sideways glance was brilliantly alive, shocking really against the dark copper mask of his face.

"That's the whole trouble, isn't it, Toni? Nothing is easy. Everything has to be paid for, some time or other. What happened this morning wasn't really your fault, so I don't blame you entirely. I should have sent you back a good hour ago. That's the whole, plain truth of it!" His tone was a hard mixture of exasperation and self-contempt.

She clenched her small fist in her lap, wishing she had a quarter of her old vitality. "You know, Mr. Nyland, I really believe you should have been a preacher with a great message for the world. Women are a plain blasted nuisance – all the Lord intended them for. Waste no further time!"

He gave his white, devastating grin, doubly effective after so much arrogance. "*Not again!* What does all this go back to, flower face? When you were a little girl? Who was the tyrant then? It's fairly obvious someone or something has left an indelible mark on your mind. You're incredibly mulish and you can't bear even the lightest hand on the reins. In short, you're wild!"

"Even a mule has a soul, Mr. Nyland!" she observed with brittle scorn.

"After which observation I hardly know which way to proceed!"

"Neither do I." A sudden smile played across her face like a patina of light. "You'll always put me in the wrong in any case. A trying position, you must admit, but it's in the nature of things."

"Yes! Too bad, isn't it, and we still haven't seen the end." His glance whipped at her face with amused malice. "Never mind, this kind of experience won't hurt you. It may even be the making of you, otherwise you'll grow into one of those women who like to rule the roost! "

"I'll be glad to accept that any day! " she said reck-lessly, her creamy skin glowing with colour.

"My notion is, little one, you don't even know what it means! That kind of arrangement wouldn't suit you at all, but I'll let you come to it all by yourself. By the way, we leave in the morning! "

"In the morning? I can't be ready by then."

"There you go again! " he said with soft mockery. "The girls will pack a few things for you. I want to be back on Savannah! "

"You drive a hard bargain, Mr. Nyland."

"I do that! " He looked very sure of himself, darkly relentless. "Now we're a little older, a little wiser, a little further along in our acquaintanceship, we'll have to be on the lookout for disturbances. The promise of proximity is enough! "

"Yes, indeed! " she said tightly, a pulse beating in her throat, her lashes motionless against her flushed cheeks. "We can't alarm Elissa or the little girl."

"That's the deal! " he stressed briefly. "So try to inject a little civility into the set-up! "

Her eyes sparkled like jets. "I'd be glad to, in fact I want to make a real contribution. I'll put you right at the centre of things, though you might find it hard to believe, and I promise to behave beautifully. If *you* will! "

He bit off a laugh. "Perhaps I will! After today. There's no doubt about it, you push me right off the deep end!" Without any further warning, he turned the utility off the track, running it into the tall columns of paperbarks, shutting off the ignition, a hard recklessness in his face.

"I can see that!" she said, greatly daring, excitement and tension feeding on itself.

"Shut up, you graceless, bad-tempered brat!"

"Oh, how you love to cut me down!" She was hurt, and she had borne so much valiantly. She hit out then, a token blow, like a small suffragette, but he caught her wrists, his fingers biting into her flesh.

"I'm losing my mind. I know I am!" There was an element of wry amusement in his tone. "Get a hold of yourself. Haven't you ever been told it's unseemly for little girls to hit back? Besides, it never comes off. Too unequal a contest!" He looked down at her flushed face. "Well, what are we going to do now? There's no profit in *your* idea!"

He was looking at her with such cool sensuality that she burst out in passionate refusal:

"Don't you dare!"

"All these great big threats!" There was a reflection of her own mood in his face, the underlying antagonism. Damon pulled her into his arms, his hand threading through her hair. "I'm glad you don't have to put up with them. You'd never have the patience. Women! What hopeless propositions! You expect them to jump one way and they jump the other!"

Toni's heart was racing so that she could scarcely

recover her breath. Some spark was between them so strong it was almost crackling. Her stretched nerves could stretch no further. Everything inside her was mounting to a crescendo. It was useless to deny it. Her eyes, huge and velvety as a faun's, filled with tears and her lower lip trembled. Damon muffled some exclamation and bent his head, fully aroused, parting her mouth, twisting her head, kissing her with such calculating artistry that her capacity to respond was brilliantly, effortlessly exploited. She was mindless, weightless, spinning in a void without end. Every sensation, every longing, everything she was. Wave upon wave of brilliance broke over her so that she shifted in his hard grasp, an instinctive, half blind, yielding movement that brought her closer against him, seared by a surge of wildest delight. It didn't seem possible, but she yearned for him. A frightening, impermanent elation. Yet she responded as if hypnotised, her mouth under his irresistibly sweet, very young and ardent, with no taste for freedom at all. All barriers were gone, all conflicts, all differences, yet it was slavery of a sort, for her own personality was subjugated.

When he lifted his head, his voice was pitched low enough to deceive her.

"What's it all about, Toni?"

She didn't try to answer him. She couldn't. Unquestionably he had the advantage, her hair fanned out over his wrist. He gave a mocking smile. "You don't dissemble very well, do you? I would say *that* was the only area you haven't found a complaint for."

Her mouth was still sensitised, pulsing with colour, a physical mark he had left upon her. She answered finally, pushed to the limit to match his sophistication.

"Does that apply to you as well, Mr. Nyland?"

He hesitated in brief indecision, unusual for him. "Sex attraction, Toni," he said in his beautiful voice. "A signal beacon, and you've got it stronger than most!"

She stared at him fascinated. "Don't think for one moment I'm offering myself as the next victim!"

"Really, you could do worse!"

She wanted to hit him, so badly – turn primitive, retaliate for that cool, mocking drawl, but his hands were ready, waiting, in case she had the same urge to repeat past mistakes.

His eyes were full of a brilliant irony, seeing her abandon her tormenting desire. "All right!" He straightened abruptly and shrugged his wide shoulders. "A lesson for both of us. We *all* do mad things. That settled, we can proceed with my plan. And don't you dare doublecross me!"

There was a shivery, destructive quality in his voice. Toni had to defend herself. Pointedly she withdrew to the furthest edge of the seat, but he only smiled.

"Needless to say you can trust me from now on, if that's what's worrying you."

"I trust no one. Not even myself," she said very quickly, trying to smooth her tangled hair. "Certainly not myself. You know so well how to exploit a weakness!"

"*Weakness?*" He injected a terrific amount of mockery into the one word. "Why, my sweet little innocent, what you've got is a great strength! You're winning all the time!"

His face was vivid with satire, his eyes on her mouth a caress by remote control. Her skin tightened electrically and she looked away from him with extreme temperament, her small face intense. *A piece in a pattern!* She was no more than that. All the hard, disturbing charm in the world couldn't dissuade her of that. From now on, every minute, every hour, she would be alert to the danger of his appeal. To her mind. To her senses, more persuasive than reason ever could be.

What she hid from herself was, it was already too late. Much, much too late. To face it would have been to look into some magical, terrifying mirror that revealed events before their time. Day-to-day living was a series of little concealments behind which most men and women chose to hide.

CHAPTER SIX

The cattle kingdom that was Savannah lay basking in the sun, casting its giant arms to left and to right; verdant from the onset of the rains, dotted with lagoons and lakes and a long silver chain of billabongs that in the months to come would link up, each floating its lively waxy burden of lotus blooms; ivory and hyacinth and palest pink, ecstatic with the sounds of the wild waterfowl; the whole landscape not so very different from Mandargi, Toni argued, if one left aside the obvious superiority of the all-weather airstrip.

Five minutes later they reached the massive wrought iron gates that led to Savannah's Big House and its satellite buildings, and she was jolted into an immediate revaluation. A curly black head and a chocolate brown face loomed up behind the lacy grill, there was a quick responsive smile, an alert half friendly, half formal salute, then the gates opened like magic without human aid and they were through.

Up the long drive they went, like the wind, past sentinel rows of coconut palms that waved their long fronds to a blazing blue sky. Flashes of the outbuildings through the screen of trees, a longer glimpse of a bungalow about the size of Mandargi's homestead, surrounded by its own gardens in full, flaunting colour. Toni missed nothing, as she looked through the windscreen and the Land Rover window, trying to keep pleasant interest and not just plain envy firmly implanted on her face.

"Satisfied?" Damon asked, the first words he had spoken in the five-mile trip in from the airstrip.

"Your fame went before you!" she said lightly. "I hardly expected modest surroundings."

"You haven't seen the house yet," he pointed out rather dryly. "It was only completed about two years ago, on the site of the original old homestead. Not unlike Mandargi's, but bigger. That had to go. Look now, it's the best angle of all."

They made a broad sweep in the drive and Toni did as she was told, the breeze coming in warmly against her face.

"Oh!" she murmured, totally inadequately, but it was the best she could manage for a while.

He slanted a glance at her profile and she turned to meet his gaze. "It's never a good idea to fall in love with someone else's property. I was trying to remind myself of it."

"Chancey, indeed!" he agreed. "But realisation usually comes slowly if it's allowed to come at all!"

"Well, I'm lost, and I might as well admit it. Right from the beginning. This could be Mandargi with a spare fortune poured into it!"

"This, my girl, is *Savannah*, and don't you forget it!"

"How could I?" she asked, surprised by the crispness of his tone. "Savannah is beautiful." Or more accurately, beautifully dramatic, she thought. A big house in the Spanish idiom, well suited to the rugged terrain, the climate, and a particular way of life.

Damon Nyland, the cattle baron! she thought with wry admiration. The do-it-yourself king of the castle. *Savannah! My more concrete assets*, as he'd put it himself. Well, he had a pretty good life going for him. Handsome, wealthy, ultra-sophisticated, a benevolent big landowner, a type all but extinct in modern times.

They were within a few hundred yards of the house, sweeping past the great spherical clumps of pampas grass with its shining silver-grey spears held meticulously to attention. Toni looked her fill. The house was big, very big, covering a considerable area, built on the highest point of the land, almost a hill, a curious mixture of stark and ornate. High white walls, arched windows, cool quarry-tiled colonnades, the decorative black ironwork repeated everywhere. It was a fascinating blend of the old world with all the vigour and know-how of the new.

They pulled into the inner court and he helped her out of the vehicle in silence, letting her absorb her surroundings. The "outer" entrance, or garden court, was paved with patterned ceramic tiles in a rich amber and brown. One ornamental wall of black wrought iron, in contrast to the stark white façade, an open timber pergola, stained black, white wrought iron furniture and huge brass pots full of the lush tropical plants of the north, some of them flowering profusely. Trellised vines, giant ferns, beautiful hanging baskets, massed succulents.

"Well?" he asked.

"Fabulous!" Toni swung her bright head to smile at him, a smile with its own subtle excitement. "Nothing to be gained by adding to that!"

"Slow coming," he drawled, his eyes on her mouth, "but a very gratifying response, Miss Stewart. I've been holding my breath, up until now. Come in by all means. I'll get someone to take your luggage through in a moment."

She took a little anticipatory breath and walked into the formal entrance. It was coolly beautiful and she could have clapped her hands like a child at a wholly pleasing spectacle. A superbly hand-carved mirror, a matching table beneath, a flanking armchair in the same style – all antiques. A brilliantly coloured ceramic plate about eighteen inches in diameter on a stand; a Malayan weeping banyan in a dully gleaming brass pot, an integral part of the decoration.

The quarry tiles extended right through the living area with exotic scatter rugs that she took to be in the Moorish style but were, in fact, as she later found out, aboriginal, specially commissioned. Paintings galore, a lot of modern abstracts, glowing like jewels, wonderfully illuminated, against the stark white walls. Above her head light fittings, in brass and bronze glass, works of art in themselves. Not a square inch that didn't excite the attention. Pieces of sculpture or something she wanted desperately to look at, placed strategically here and there.

"Someone has an unerring eye!" she said with unfeigned fervour. "A very special way of doing things!"

"Me!"

She smiled at that, thinking it typical, and touched a reverent finger to a beautiful chest decorated with inlaid ivory. "I'm not in the least surprised. Oriental?"

"Chinese."

"If you've got it, you've got it, and if you haven't, I suppose you can always pay a decorator."

"Not me, flower face. I choose what I have to live with. No one else has unloaded their ideas on me. So far!"

"With stunning results, Mr. Nyland!"

"*Damon*, from now on, if you don't mind. You give that 'Mr. Nyland' double value as if you didn't know. No, spare me the wide-eyed look. I find independence in a woman intolerable!"

"Faint wonder you're a bachelor! Which is a pity. A certain amount of training is necessary for all of us!"

"Oh, I agree," he said suavely, "but some men are just too plain dodgy to ever get caught. Anyone who lives with a woman will tell you the whole situation is fraught with difficulties, like walking through a mine-field! As for myself, I've always found women either regard me as a wonderful meal ticket or . . ."

". . . please don't undersell yourself!" Toni burst out tartly, and with considerable truth.

"Either way you can't win." His eyes were brilliant with amused mockery roving over her face, sparking an immediate response.

"Perhaps you're right at that! Trying to domesticate *you* would never prove entirely satisfactory. It almost calls for a silent tribute to a lot of brave women, and I'm sure there *have* been a lot of them!"

"The usual kind of thing," he agreed suavely. "That's the really great thing about women, their endless tenacity. That appears to be an undisputed fact. Anything else is in the region of folklore, I'm afraid."

"Then you'd better watch out for yourself, hadn't you?" she said pleasantly. "You *will* marry?"

"I said so, didn't I? I would dearly love a son to inherit all this, without causing the most impossible scandal!"

She moved away from him in a series of graceful little swirls, coming to rest beside a brass inlaid cabinet. "You may not even have to pick out a wife," she suggested blithely. "She might pick you out. Wouldn't that be a surprise?"

"The inevitable must come, by any one of the various methods. Who knows, you may be trying out one yourself!" He had come up behind her and she felt the strength draining out of her limbs, her heart hammering against her ribs. She swung to face him, tilting her chin.

"Oh, that's brilliant! A charmingly sentimental theory. There's not a man from nine to ninety who doesn't think somebody's after him!"

"You've got a lot of disastrous ideas yourself," he said in a voice that panicked her for all its light mockery. "Now why the long, desolate look? You've got beautiful eyes, Toni — large, lustrous, long-lashed. A pity you're so difficult and quarrelsome. You'll be all the better for being supervised and directed on Savannah."

The faint indulgence melted all her resentments away. She laughed, a pretty three-noted sound. "Don't expect me to flinch away, though I can see you're going to be pretty much in control of things. Around here, at any rate!"

"So act accordingly," he warned, "even if we can expect a certain amount of trouble during the adjustment period. You'll have to admit we haven't hit it off all that well, up to now. Come now, Toni, tell me, what do you think of the furniture? You can't ignore it any more with our usual chit-chat."

She slithered away from him smoothly, away from those baffling light eyes. "Custom-designed?" she asked lightly.

"Yes, it had to be. Scaled to the volume of space,

if you know what I mean!" He made no attempt to follow her up, leaning an elbow on top of the cabinet, only his eyes tracking her.

She replied in mocking imitation. "I do, indeed! In fact, I don't think I'd move anything six inches either way."

"A fantastic admission for a woman!"

"Maybe." She let her eyes run over the grouped sofas, the deep armchairs, the fabrics, linen and silk and wool.

"I hate clutter," he announced almost to himself. "Being hemmed in."

She turned to regard him in some astonishment. "Well, you've plenty of space here. I'd be more likely to clatter in a place this size!"

His clear green eyes lit with amused malice. "My darling girl, perhaps we move in different social circles. On Savannah we have twenty guests at a time, every other week-end. Spare a moment to take that in. I don't usually accommodate them one on top of the other – not unless they specifically ask for it!"

"The more the merrier!" she said, effortlessly sweet. "I've always taken that with a grain of salt myself. I stand chastised!"

"For how long?"

"That's *your* fault, in my opinion!" she said, refusing to look at him.

Damon did what she always least expected. He laughed. Evidently she amused him. He uncoiled his elegant long length and came towards her. "I'll take you down to the wine cellar when I know you better, but for now, we'll content ourselves with the pool area."

Like an exasperated but intensely preoccupied child she followed him through the curving archways of tinted glass backed by black wrought iron, the glass reducing the glare from the aquamarine pool. They were out on a roofed terrace, an idyllic and secluded outdoor living area, a dazzling and fascinating array of the lovely Donna Aurora, a tropical flowering shrub, creamy and more compact than the ever-present bougainvillea. They were arranged in green glazed Chinese pots beside the smooth white steps that led to the pool.

"It's a nice old place, isn't it?" Toni asked with some humour, looking into his dark, sardonic face, lit by the same brand of taste. "I'll never be able to settle down again. Savannah will be too difficult to forget!"

"Maybe I won't let you forget me either," he said, low and mocking.

"As long as we can still be friends after!" She avoided his eyes, feeling softly shaken, her own eyes brilliantly dark, fully conscious of the terrible burden of attraction.

He smiled unexpectedly and ran a finger down her small, straight nose. "I ought to be ashamed of myself. I'm forgetting how old you are. Still, Elissa and

110

young Annette will be here by this afternoon. They tell me children make the best chaperones!"

His voice was so very attractive, with that hint of a laugh in it, Toni smiled, her mouth curving rather dreamily, had she known it.

"Damon, you're back!"

A woman was behind them, standing at the top of the stairs, one hand shading her eyes – tall, rather angular, very plainly but neatly dressed, an apron. A competent, no-nonsense type with intelligent, understanding eyes, anywhere between fifty and sixty, exceedingly plain until she smiled, then her face lit up in a quite remarkable fashion.

"Clarrie!" Damon turned to her with ease and considerable affection.

"I did so want to make a good impression standing by the door and all that, but a few other things claimed my attention!" She smiled directly into Toni's face and Toni felt her own face softening. There was a genuineness about that smile and it impressed itself on her mind.

Damon introduced them serenely, watching his housekeeper come down the steps, her hand outstretched.

"Mrs. Chase – Clarrie, when she comes to accept you – Toni Stewart, our young neighbour from Mandargi, and house guest for a week or so."

"How are you, my girl?" Clarissa Chase took Toni's hand in a terrible grip and looked intently into

111

her face. "None the worse for your adventures? We all listen to the galah sessions, you know."

"I'm fine, thank you, Mrs. Chase," Toni said, unobtrusively flexing her numbed fingers. "Mr. Nyland put a few stitches in a gash in my arm and it's almost right again."

"You look simply beautiful," Clarissa Chase said firmly. "I'd have given my eye teeth to have looked like you as a girl. That brother of yours wasn't behind the door either. Good-lookers, the pair of you. Good bones. Good blood. We'll marry you off in no time!"

"Clarrie always speaks her mind!" Damon said in a calm drawl.

"Don't worry, I'm going!" Clarrie turned on him. "I just came to say welcome and hello."

"Thank you, Mrs. Chase," Toni said quickly. "That was very kind of you."

Clarissa Chase didn't hesitate for a moment. "We can't go on like this – Clarrie it is. We must think of the future! Now, if there's anything you want, any time, call me. I'm never out of the kitchen, though some days I'm sure Damon here is only waiting for me to turn in my notice so he can get a more suitable replacement."

"Now, now, Clarrie, after ten eventful years, even *I* can't turn you out!"

That proved more effective than the most flowery metaphors. Mrs. Chase went off beaming, and was presently out of sight.

"Clarrie's just that little bit outspoken," Damon said, his attention returning to Toni. "In fact, some of my guests have found her downright odd!"

"That's all right, I like her," Toni said simply. "I was brought up to speak my mind!"

"You can say *that* again!" he said in full, round tones, turning to smile at her. "You're a determined little cuss, but don't let's wrangle about it. I'll show you your room. A girl like you would be quite particular where she sleeps."

"For the most part, I can take good care of myself," she said quite without thinking, a challenging set to her glittery head.

"We all make mistakes from time to time," he supplied smoothly, a flash of sarcasm in his vibrant voice, "but come along and tell me what you think. I like to gather as much information as I can about my house guests."

He turned and led the way across the central court, tall and lean, powerful shoulders, his dark masculinity, a live thing. She followed more slowly, watching him open the sliding glass doors of a room that opened out on to the pool area.

"All the guest rooms are essentially the same," he said, looking down at her, one arm on the side of the door, a taunting kind of courtesy in his cool eyes. "Colour variations, that sort of thing. You can take your pick. I thought you might be happy here, but I suppose you'll settle for something else purely as a gesture of defiance!"

He had his back to the light, his height exaggerated, almost hypnotic in his stillness.

"Now that would be a dead give-away, wouldn't it?" she said, edging to get past him, to no avail. "I thought it took years and years to know a person as well as that."

He relented his position, shifting his arm, pushing the door to its furthest limits. "I don't think so, Toni. You're relatively simple — to follow, that is. I don't mean for a moment you're dim-witted. Never that!"

"May I see, please, Mr. Nyland, you dreadful man?" Her dark eyes sparkled up at him.

"Why not?"

She brushed past him, on line with his shoulder. A rare co-ordination of movement, as slender as a tulip. "I'll be well and truly incommunicado out here!" she said, coming to rest in the centre of the room.

"The point is, you won't bother me any," he supplied sardonically.

"Point taken! If it's of any consequence, I'll be more than happy here. In fact, I'm greatly indebted to you."

"I'm so pleased!" He glanced at her tilted young profile, his green eyes shimmering with amusement. "Elissa and the little girl will stay in the main wing. I thought you'd appreciate your own private world. As you can see, it's entirely self-contained. If you scream at night, just make sure it's loud enough!"

Toni shook her bright head and her hair made magical moves against her cheeks. "That's very unlikely!" she said loftily. His eyes had the power to transfix her, so she avoided them carefully. "Tell me, why did you think this was me?" She gestured around the beautifully appointed room — teak, inbuilt furniture, a deep armchair, a small bookcase, a writing desk and a chair.

"Autumn leaf colours!" he supplied in a silky drawl.

She smiled and her eyes moved to the thick, luxurious bedspread, deeply fringed and patterned in rust and gold, a rich brown and a bright orange. "Woodsy, in fact!"

"Anything but! I think you're very bold and adventurous, for a girl, not to speak of eye-catching — but for now I must leave you. Not before time. There'll be plenty to catch up on even after a few days' absence." He threw up his head, preparing to leave, and Toni surprised in herself an odd kind of reaction. She pressed an instinctive hand to the base of her throat. He was still talking, his dark head in silhouette against the brilliant light.

"Don't be afraid to wander around at will. There are quite a few things to interest you, I feel sure. The pool — always supposing you can swim!"

She smiled, a little ironically. "Float, at any rate! Which is what I'm doing right now. I daren't go with the tide!"

He turned to flicker her a look of urbane charm. "You're quite a girl, Toni. I only hope Elissa likes you."

"So do I," she confided. "I couldn't bear to offend your family."

"I honestly think you'll make out, if you try hard enough," he said soothingly. "Well, so long, little one. Clarrie likes you, at any rate. No small thing. I can't speak for myself – as yet!"

A full thirty seconds elapsed before Toni felt able to move again. If the worst really came to the worst and Elissa found her less than compatible, she could always make a bolt for home. One thing stood her in good stead – she had come to Savannah with the best possible intentions!

Elissa was pure Meissen, a petite aristocrat, a delicate piece of porcelain to round off a collection. Annette, her little girl, was pure Nyland, a holy terror of six going on seven, completely inexplicable to her mother, but very pretty with glossy dark curls, a peachy skin and the now predictable light eyes. They flew in towards late afternoon on a charter flight in the company of Keith Hammond, of Hammond, Hampshire Sinclair, the Nyland family solicitors. It was unthinkable that Elissa Nyland should have travelled alone.

From the very first instant Toni met Elissa's Siamese stare, she knew it was an error to have been invited, for Elissa had no need of female companionship, never had, never would. Elissa Nyland was a very calculating feline, and one of her quirks was *never sharing*, with anyone. She had a whole bag of tricks that further enhanced her fragile, boneless elegance, one of them being to let her hand hover tentatively in the air for a moment before coming to rest in the crook of a man's arm – Damon's, Keith Hammond's, a pleasant, well-spoken man in his early forties, who met this little endearing gesture with an expectant look. It would have been immediately apparent to a blind man that Keith Hammond was smitten, enslaved.

Toni stood well back admiring while Elissa trod delicately through the house in a pretty, mysterious manner, pale silver head bobbing, surveying her new home, all the while purring how "extravagantly tired" she was, the upshot of which was that Toni was left with the child, who had slept on the plane and as a result was now as tranquil as a firecracker.

An hour later in the kitchen, Toni's spirits had reached a rock-bottom low as the child gave a consistent "Yuck!" to everything that was offered to her in the way of light nourishment. Clarrie, busy with her own preparations for what promised to be a banquet, watched the small circus in a telling silence, until finally, well ahead with her own duties, she trained on Annette a look of extreme practicality.

"You're a little miracle and no mistake. A mix and

match angel!" She shifted her grey gaze to Toni's flushed young face. "You go and have a swim, cool off before dinner. It's hot enough. I'll deal with young madam here!"

Whether the old terminology was entirely new to Annette or because she could detect a certain look in Clarrie's unswerving gaze, she fell to drinking her milk with saucer-eyed attention, intensely curious but not unfriendly after the initial moment of sceptical surprise. Unconcernedly Clarrie broke eggs into a bowl and frothed them up with a dash of milk and a sprinkle of salt.

"Scrambled eggs on fingers of toast be all right?"

"Yes, thank you, Mrs. Chase," said Annette, in every way a most amenable child.

Toni reached the kitchen door and saluted Clarrie over the glossy dark head. "You've a very useful personality, Clarrie. No wonder at all Damon won't part with you!"

The glance she had returned to her was amused and disarming. "Didn't you know I had four of my own?"

"No, really?"

"Three boys and a girl. All married, all on the land. Eight or nine grandchildren. Even I've lost count of them. After a while you get to know every trick of the trade. All this child needs is a little home psychology!"

"Don't we all!" Toni was looking at Annette's

bent head, startled by the radical change in the child's manner. It was complete surrender, for she had calmed down and was ready and actually willing to fork into the fluffy yellow pile.

"There's always a way round a tricky situation," Clarrie said complacently, placing the plate before the child.

"Well, you certainly solved my problem. Thank you!" Toni said with a spontaneous smile.

Clarrie looked for a moment at the gay, laughing face. "Don't thank me. You'll do. Now go off and enjoy yourself. I'll look after Annette. Not that I know it's either of our jobs!"

The light fell across the curve of Toni's cheek so that her skin seemed dazzling. Both women exchanged a look that said plainly Elissa couldn't have cared less. There was a silence, then Toni cast a sidelong look at the little girl's tranquil profile.

"I haven't had much to do with children, but they certainly appeal to me. My first attempt at managing was pretty hopeless, though!"

"You'll come to it. We all do," Clarrie promised strongly.

With an odd half defensive, half excited look, Annette opened her beautiful, rosebud mouth. "May I come for a swim with you, please, Toni?"

Clarrie laughed and suddenly pressed the curly dark head against her breast. "There, what did I tell you? Not tonight, my lamb, tomorrow perhaps. Now I have some nice vanilla ice-cream. Sauce on top, do you think?"

"Chocolate, thank you," Annette said in a dainty voice, shoving her plate away. "Good-bye, Toni."

Toni smiled at both of them and walked out of the room in a much more mellow frame of mind. The rest of the house was quite silent, like a household in thrall. As she walked slowly and lingeringly through the beautiful rooms, a vision floated out into the hall-way. A fairy child. No, too much sex appeal for that, Toni reasoned with reluctant admiration, gritting her teeth for the moment of encounter. A wonderful omen for the next few weeks.

"Don't rush away!" the vision said, swaying to-wards her.

Pretending a warmth and friendliness she did not feel, and vaguely ashamed of herself, Toni gave her lovely, natural smile.

"How are you feeling now, Mrs. Nyland?"

Elissa tinkled into a little laugh of admission. "Quite bleak, actually, but you could make life just a teeny bit easier for me, if you would."

"I'd consider it a privilege," Toni said pleasantly, steeling herself to avoid her own ironic reflection in a gilt-scrolled mirror.

"That's nice!" Elissa responded in her silver-clear, well-bred voice. She eyed Toni speculatively, as though trying to penetrate her façade. A queen, who had acquired a new and unlikely lady-in-waiting.

120

She was very petite, a porcelain figurine, an inch or so over five feet, so that she was obliged to lift her violet-blue eyes to Toni's. "I've tried to be tolerant, but really; the house-girls! I know they're well trained, but . . . would you be a darling and unpack my things? I honestly can't face it, and I don't care to see . . ." She snapped off right there with an air of extreme fastidiousness, which was, nevertheless, entirely natural, generous in her adversity, leaving it to Toni to decipher her meaning.

Toni saw only too well. No slim chocolate brown hands among the silks and the chiffons and the laces. The shining ash-blonde head was still tilted, the arching throat white as a swan's, the narrow tilted eyes steady and unswerving, one hand gently stroking the pale, soft hair at the nape of her neck. Her peignoir was exquisite, an indescribable mixture of blue and hyacinth, enfolding and caressing the slight figure in the subtlest revealing fashion. It was hard to say exactly how old she was, for a whole world of sophistication gleamed out of the narrow eyes, upsetting Toni's first verdict of about twenty-seven. Elissa, was, in fact, thirty-two, and even she had forgotten it.

"You haven't said – how is Annette?" Her smile was bright, her voice sweetly amiable, so that Toni wondered why she doubted its genuineness.

"Mrs. Chase is looking after her," she explained. "She's settled down quite well and she's having her tea. I've just come from the kitchen now."

"I'm very, very, grateful. I did wonder, Miss Stewart, if you'd come *now*!"

"Yes, of course." For the first time, her true role on Savannah hit Toni starkly in the eye. There was more than a touch of regal arrogance in the request. Well, she *had* offered!

Elissa turned away, her negligée swirling in a mist about her feet. "I do hope you won't be bored to tears in the next week or so. There's so very little I shall require of you. Rest is all I need, peace of mind – precious, up until now *unattainable* commodities. But you could be of great help with Annette, take her off my hands. I did want to ask you if you would mind having her beside you at night until the governess arrives. She's been very restless at night. I have such indifferent health – hard to accept sometimes!" She gave a little expressive movement of her hands, obviously waiting for Toni's assent.

"I wouldn't mind in the least," Toni found herself saying, mildly enough, "but I'm sure, Mrs. Nyland, she'd much rather be beside you."

"Of course, but it's not possible at the moment. You do see that? I must get a full night's sleep or I'm good for nothing. *Honestly!*" Elissa paused for a moment, her mouth smiling softly. "Damon is so good to me – too good, really. I'll never, never be able to repay him, but of course he won't hear a word of thanks. I think he *loves* doing it anyway, and he's so terribly taken with Annette!"

For the life of her, Toni couldn't come up with an answer to that, being as it was complete news to her. Elissa, however, was indifferent to her reaction. She reached the door of her room, smiling across at Toni, her Siamese blue eyes conveying some wonderful secret she was not as yet at liberty to tell. But once inside the room, she drooped with childlike weariness into an armchair, a dispossessed princess, tapping a very white hand to her lips.

"I do so envy you your robust health. You're quite a good-looking girl!"

Toni, her dark eyes amused and just a little bit cynical, looked about her, hardly hearing Elissa's barbed compliment. The room was a tribute to Elissa's beauty and graciousness, fitting for "family". One of the two master suites, it comprised a bedroom and bath-dressing area beyond, the height of luxury in terms of space and furnishings, glowing in its white and gold shell. In a house of collections, here and there, reposed some exquisite "object" such as would never have found its way into a guest room, elegant as they might be. And looking, Toni knew beyond all doubt that Damon Nyland had gauged correctly the guest of honour. Elissa fitted all this as though it had been planned for her. Shocking to think it had! But of course it couldn't. Time was against her. Suddenly, passionately, Toni wished it might have been hers, then cold reason came to her rescue and she resolved never to have that particular thought again.

Elissa lifted her slim brows and gave her shoulders the tiniest shrug. "Perhaps you could run my bath, dear, before you start on my clothes. I know you'll be careful. I do have such lovely things!"

You beaut! Toni thought to herself dismally. *Run my bath?* Almost for a moment she nearly told Elissa what she could do, then in her apathy decided she didn't care. She disappeared into the room beyond in her dual role of nanny and unpaid lady's help.

It was a sacrilege to walk on the pale, lovely rugs, so she didn't, keeping to the tiled part of the floor. While she ran water into the oval tub set with pale opaline tiles, she heard Elissa's silvery voice, raised in summons, just loud enough to be heard above the rushing water. Toni walked back into the bedroom just in time to see Elissa point out a largish vanity case that contained her lotions and perfumes and creams. In another minute an elusive expensive fragrance wafted through the two rooms as Toni emptied bath salts into the running water.

On the tiled counter that ran the length of one wall she set out jar after jar, each promising eternal beauty, not a one of them able to bestow the vaguest illusion where there was none. At last it was all over and done with and abundantly clear that Elissa disregarded not one inch of herself in the relentless war against time. Back in the bedroom, Toni walked briskly back and forth, from the bed to the wardrobes, and bureaux, taking the greatest care of Elissa's "lovely things",

124

her luminous eyes wide and pensive.

Elissa, in a brocade armchair, sat, a creature apart, and indeed it was impossible to believe she could be anything else. Her taste and her clothes were perfect, Toni learned. She must have also a great deal of money, which meant that one inevitably escaped the more menial tasks like unpacking for oneself. As well, she made no attempt to spin a web of small talk or enliven the proceedings with a small smile of thanks, but sat thinking her own thoughts, or perhaps a plan of campaign, like a woman at the hairdressers, her beautiful robe pulled about her excessive fragility.

"There, that should do it." Toni pushed the bureau drawer shut and turned to the silent Elissa. "Perhaps as Annette is to come with me I should shift her things now – or would you rather keep her this one night so she can settle in?"

"No, no!" Elissa came right out of her brooding trance, her words so nearly shrill that Toni was momentarily startled. "That will be quite all right," she smiled in the sweetest possible fashion, putting the brakes on. "For all my vigilance, Annette has become very naughty lately, and on top of all my own problems, I've found it rather a strain. It's not as though I'm strong, and we won't be isolated. I shall be seeing as much of her as I can."

She spoke as if her child was a natural hazard, not without love, but more as if her own offspring acted at times as a parasitic vine to pull Elissa down.

125

"Well, in that case," Toni said dryly, "I'll take her things now. Where are they, by the way?"

Elissa lifted her left arm in a purely balletic gesture. "The two blue cases over there. One is full of her toys. She won't go anywhere without them, and of course I have to give in to her on every point. It's not as if they were her best either. She has magnificent things!"

Lovely things! Magnificent things! Toni returned to the chatter ... "the *Gregory* Nylands, that is, my late people. They spoil her dreadfully. She's such a beauful child. I think somehow Damon imagined she would be beside me, but of course he's not familiar with our pattern. It's very good of you, Miss Stewart, to do all this for me, though Damon explained that he's paying you for your services, so I don't feel so badly."

With an effort Toni controlled her runaway tongue. "Actually, Mrs. Nyland, you've been misinformed, but don't let it bother you in any way. I'm here in a purely friendly capacity."

"You are?"

From the height of Elissa's silken brows and with a rising heart Toni grasped intuitively that Damon had mentioned nothing whatever about payment. That was Elissa's own little testing thrust.

"Neighbourly, that's all," she continued, in a light, even voice. "My brother Paul leases Mandargi from Mr. Nyland. It's on Savannah's boundary."

"Yes, I know. Quite a jump up for a young man."

"Paul is extremely capable, a very go-ahead young man. I'm sure Damon told you *that*!"

"Actually, no," Elissa pointed out, regarding her shell pink nails. "He said very little beyond the few necessary facts. There were so many important things to catch up on. My husband was Damon's first cousin, did you know? I only met Damon at my own wedding. He'd been in the States before that. I believe he was always the bright boy of the family. Naturally I inherit my husband's shares in Nyland Holdings. Who knows, in a sense, I might be your employer as well?" She looked up at Toni with a bright smile.

"I think you'll find Mandargi is listed among Damon Nyland's *private* assets," Toni said quite matter-of-factly. "I imagine that would apply to Savannah as well, although I wouldn't really know."

"No, Savannah's Damon's. I checked," Elissa admitted artlessly.

"How interesting! Did you ever see the old homestead, Mrs. Nyland?"

"My dear!" Elissa used her hands again in genuine horrified remembrance. "It was frightful. Primitive by my standards. I couldn't have borne to have stayed here then. Believe it or not, Damon *did*, on and off for years while he developed all his projects. It was one of those old, old, shambling buildings, a Colonial-type bungalow. I can't imagine, knowing what kind of man Damon is, how he tolerated it!"

127

"First things first, I suppose," Toni said, seeing the funny side of it. "I rather like the old bungalows myself. We have one on Mandargi. I hope I've made it attractive and comfortable, though it would probably fit into Savannah's swimming pool. Speaking of swimming pools, do you mind if Annette takes a dip with me? Can she swim?"

"No, she can't!" Elissa lightly pointed out. "I can't either, for that matter. I'd detest all those chemicals on my skin. But teach Annette by all means – if you can!"

"There shouldn't be any problem about that. I had a whole sideboard of silver cups in my schooldays."

"How nice!" Elissa smiled up at her doubtfully. "Then I feel quite happy about leaving her with you. I'm anxious to learn as much as I can about Savannah. It's Damon's life, you see."

"A very isolated life in many ways," Toni said rather flatly, trying not to see.

"But my dear!" Elissa gave her high, sweet laugh. "Damon is here, there, and everywhere. You simply don't know where he'll turn up. No one could ever say Damon Nyland stays in the one place. He just uses Savannah as a jumping-off point. It's a very profitable enterprise, I understand. I know nothing, but *nothing*, about livestock. Breeding, that kind of thing." Some new sensuous intonation crept into her voice. "Not that Damon would care. He only likes very *feminine* women. He has superb taste in everything.

128

He had a marvellous education and he's travelled so widely. It does make a difference!"

"Yes, he certainly has more than his fair share of everything!"

It was Elissa's turn for a setback. Her eyes narrowed and she glanced up in surprise. "But, my dear, you sound as if you don't like him?"

"I *admire* him tremendously, Mrs. Nyland," Toni said portentously. "It doesn't really matter whether I like him or not. Now if you'll excuse me, I'll take Annette's things and unpack them before dinner."

"Good idea!" Elissa's gleaming eyes were abstracted, falling on Toni vaguely as though she hardly saw her. After a moment she stood up, her slight body arching, her silvery head lifted, smiling patiently at Toni, obviously waiting for her to go. The small, boneless hand was deftly touching the soft hair at the nape of her neck again.

"If I have to," she promised sweetly, "I can testify that you're an excellent lady's maid! Thank you again."

Toni was less than amused, but it would be impossible to defeat a woman like Elissa. Somewhere along the line Elissa had lost the capacity or the interest to talk to her own sex, or perhaps she truly thought Toni of no consequence, just another one on the Nyland payroll. It was rather terrible to be judged by the criterion of money and success.

Gently she said with impeccable courtesy, "I'll see

you at dinner, then, Mrs. Nyland."

For the first time Elissa allowed herself to survey the younger woman thoroughly. Her tilted eyes travelled all over Toni from her feet to her face, her small mouth quirked. Finally her face assumed an expression of wanting to help.

"You know, dear, you'd be much more of a success with a little more dress sense, though I don't suppose it matters up here!"

For some reason Toni was seized by the wild impulse to laugh. The calculation behind the apparent artlessness! The beginnings of a smile touched her mouth. "I can't take all the blame, Mrs. Nyland," she said lightly. "Damon picked this. We were in an awful rush to leave Mandargi."

Elissa's face was a study, a series of expressions rippling over her face, but Toni had missed them. She picked up the cases, one in each hand, and walked unhurriedly out of the room.

CHAPTER SEVEN

It was a beautiful day, golden and friendly, just a few curls of cirrus cloud in the perfect peacock blue of the sky. The water of the Blue Lady billabong was made warm and lazy, idling along, a life-giving stream, secretively beautiful, very deep in spots with a pandanus palm that grew crookedly over the bank to make a splendid diving board. Toni had already made use if it, enjoying every moment of her swim, but now she sat with Annette, further upstream where the water shallowed, for here there were lots of polished stones for Annette to play with.

She sat beside Toni, childishly absorbed, dabbling her toes, her pink dress crumpled, damp around the hem, stained with the bright green moss that grew all over the big boulders. She was happy and content, one of her good days, may-it-last, endlessly rearranging her pile of stones with a few wild flowers thrown in and some bright, shiny leaves. The bank under the trees was cool and fragrant with the scent of the acacias, the bush boronia and a narrow-leafed shrub that was heavy with pale lavender flowers.

High up above them, a herd of cattle were making the journey along an established cattle pad, the young bulls thudding, a rhythmic drumming, thrusting boughs aside with their wide horn-span. A flock of rosellas that lay along the branches of the paperbarks, sunning themselves and chatting gaily, took to the skies in a clean, shining sweep, a bright, alarmed cloud that swirled upwards effortlessly. Toni looked from the lovely flash of colours to the child, surveying her tender nape with a kind of wry affection. Funny little scrap she was, all but impossible for most of the time. Elissa would be horrified by the state of her pink dress.

In fact, Elissa's views on child raising differed widely from the norm. On the odd day she showed an obsessive interest in the child: her looks, her clothes, her health, her intelligence, then for the rest of the week appeared to give up the whole business as a bad job. Small wonder Annette knew no stability at all, and Toni used up every bit of her ingenuity in keeping the child harmlessly amused.

In many respects, Annette had been spoiled rotten, in others, starved of the tried and true old-fashioned methods of child management. In the fortnight or so since she had been on Savannah, the household had been treated to a round dozen temper tantrums and frequent impudent, equal-to-equal exchanges with a mother who offered no form of parental opposition. Only the droop of Elissa's slight shoulders indicated the true state of her physical and mental health.

Toni, involved, but not deeply, felt reluctant to interfere. Incredibly so did Damon, without a doubt the intended stepfather, although Toni had seen him eyeing the child thoughtfully, while her own hand itched to administer a few telling slaps. More often than not Elissa appeared locked in her ivory tower, powerless, under the spell of her own child, though it was obvious to all that Elissa would benefit from a spot of physical activity even if it were only to catch up a slipper.

But at night, with Annette a sleeping cherub, Elissa came into her own, making Toni a daily witness to a masterly display of technique in how to fascinate a man with the object of winning him, a purpose for which she was admirably equipped. By day she slumbered, attended to her beauty programme, chatted on and off to a rapt Keith Hammond, drove around the property with Damon, went on one trip to the coast with him, though they were back well before nightfall. She didn't ride and she wouldn't be caught dead within three hundred yards of a steer or a cow. But at night, with the men free to enjoy her company, she performed certain feats of magic in suggesting a warm friendliness between herself and Toni, relying heavily on the natural gullibility of the male. They were charmed and impressed and thought it no small thing that two such good-looking women should share a bond of camaraderie. If they found Toni's rapid-fire deliveries and volleys a trifle too brisk they wisely said nothing. Undoubtedly she had style. Elissa had the grace.

Elissa's attitude, however, was promptly sacrificed. dropped like a stone, on the isolated occasions when the two women stumbled on one another unawares, for they had established an unspoken agreement of scrupulous avoidance.

Every day Toni regretted her position, but regrets offered no solution. Her release would come. The governess had been hired – an English girl, doing a two-year stint of Australia and New Zealand. Her qualifications were excellent. She would arrive at the end of the month, and privately Toni mourned for her. On one infrequent occasion when she saw him alone, Damon had said he would force her into accepting a token payment, but she was not engaged in any status-seeking and told him so. Let the Nylands look to themselves. All she wanted to do was get out, away from Savannah with no harm done.

It was unbearable to watch him being so attentive, so darkly, charmingly, suavely urbane with his exquisite cream-fed relative, for far from being introspective and withdrawn as Toni had been led to believe, Elissa had come out of her shell with unprecedented abandon, witty and so slightly malicious, night-blooming, every evening in a different hostess gown, specially designed for her as she was so tiny. Wonder of wonders! as Clarrie put it, her eyes raised to the ceiling, for Elissa had a very healthy appetite. "Glory knows where she puts it!"

In short, Elissa was almost exclusively self-orientated, with a faithfulness that transcended the necessary expediencies of bringing up a small child. It would be a bitter, empty battle to goad Damon into seeing her as she really was, but in fact, Toni lacked the heart and mind for it. It would be an impossible contest in any case, for Elissa had great natural cunning and contrary to her appearance she was very strong and single-minded when it came to getting what she wanted.

Toni, motionless, sat beside Annette staring into space, her body slightly bent, like a flower on a stalk.

Now and again, with a barely perceptible motion, she passed Annette another stone to add to her collection and Annette lifted a flushed, smiling face to say "Thank you!" Poor little Annette! Nothing on Savannah was as it appeared to be. Behind Elissa's small enigmatic smile lay a scheming mind. Behind the sweet graciousness, no living warmth.

Why don't you admit it? Toni thought painfully. You're licked. Admit it and take the easy way out. There was nothing drastic about announcing that she had to be back on Mandargi. Paul had relayed a message which, decoded, said plainly that he was missing her badly. Probably Tikka and Leila didn't take kindly to being "straightened out" by a well-meaning Mrs. Carroll.

She thought too of Damon. Surely he asked more of a woman than just — Suddenly she was sickened, as much by her own endless mulling over the problem as anything else. It was none of her business in any case. She smiled to herself with some derision. She just didn't care. Now, too late, she discovered she just didn't care. Elissa's sweetness carried a wasp's sting. Damon's practised charm, which he used with such devastating success, meant nothing, absolutely nothing, and she would do best to forget it. She would have to struggle alone with her own private devils of disillusionment.

Toni ran her hand over Annette's glossy curls and the child looked up enquiringly. For a moment Toni was lost in the clear, limpid green of the Nyland eyes, feeling submerged by a quick wave of self-pity. She would have to get over it. She rose with decision.

"Come along, darling," she said lightly. "We'd better make it back to the house. It's almost four o'clock."

Annette gave an enchanting little smile and got to her feet. "We had a good time, didn't we? May I take the stones back, please, Toni? I *adore* them. Mummy won't look at them, of course. She's like that."

"Mummy's a wonderful person when she feels well," Toni said, trying to be gallant.

Annette stretched luxuriously as she watched Toni collect the pile of stones. "Mummy hates people. That includes me. She told me!"

Unable to believe it, Toni protested, "Oh, Annette darling, she doesn't. She loves you. All mothers love their children."

Annette's clear eyes were shadowed by her lashes. "*You* love children," she pointed out. "And dogs and horses and cows and everything. I'm going to stay with you, always. You're my best friend. You make up such lovely stories I want to go to bed."

Toni smiled back at her, irresistibly trapped by the Nyland charm. "When you're good, you're very, very good," she said lightly, and caught Annette's hand, holding it close and warm. "Now, *en avant!*"

Annette threw back her head. "What does that mean?"

"Get going, my pet!"

At the top of the ridge poincianas broke out like a sweep of fire, flaming everywhere one looked. The land fell into quiet – yet not quiet. The silence was enhanced by a symphony of little sounds, the rustle of the soft cane grass, the multi-throated insects, the slow slither of a lizard, wild geese that honked overhead. A breeze came and set the millions and millions of leaves sighing.

Ever afterwards, Toni never knew what focused her attention on a gaunt dead gum, bleached to the colour of bone, stripped of life, of leaf, of everything. It was picturesque in a way, surrounded by pale green saplings.

It moved! Unable to believe her eyes, Toni blinked. It *did* move, coming down slowly like a stage prop on wires, directly in their path. Blood and brightness beat in her head. She could see it all happening with dreadful clarity. She jerked up a hand to fling away the stones, made a grab for the little girl.

"The tree!" she gasped, and started to run, her heart in her mouth lest they be running in the track of the falling giant, nearly lifting Annette off the ground. She tripped and fell and Annette came down heavily on top of her. They rolled together, as with a great rending roar the great bleached column crashed to the ground, smashing saplings and anything that lay in its path.

Twigs and leaves and bits of dead timber rayed

137

through the golden spray of dust. It clogged the atmosphere, making them both cough. Toni sat up, dazed, gathering Annette on to her lap. Shaking, the child looked back at her silently, round-eyed.

"That was a close go!" Toni breathed, and gave a funny little choked laugh. "Those trees stand for years and years and suddenly they come down. I suppose it was the rain loosening the roots. Either that, or I'm accident-prone!"

"It's a fearful thing to happen!" Annette suddenly announced, her sense of hospitality outraged. "I shall tell Uncle Damon!" And up she got and made off at a spanking rate which Toni in her jittery state couldn't hope to match.

She felt her heart hammering against her ribs as she visualised Elissa's tilted eyes appraising her in open hostility. Even an act of God would take some explaining. "Look here!" she gasped, running after Annette and gripping the child's shoulder. "We won't alarm anyone. I'll tell the story myself, simply. It could have happened to any one of us."

"But it *didn't*!" Annette insisted doggedly. "It happened to us. I shall tell Mummy and Uncle Damon. I hurt myself when I toppled down."

The Land Rover was parked on a patch of grassy turf. Annette clambered in and Toni surveyed her ruined cotton slacks, pulled on over her brief swim-suit. Pieces of twig still reposed in her hair. Annette looked a sorry sight. Elissa was legally entitled to an explanation. Toni said as casually as she could, starting up the engine:

"Don't worry about it, darling. It's past history already. We were lucky! I *do* have a good after-dinner story!"

The tyres hummed and the wind cooled their cheeks. In ten minutes they were back at the house with Toni for the first time in her life as nervous as if she had conceived some monstrous plot to do away with a Nyland heiress. Annette jumped out of the Land Rover and galloped off as fast as her legs would carry her, evidently not as hurt as she thought. Still brushing her hair, Toni followed with the uneasy suspicion Annette was about to make great capital out of the incident, in the process, making a lot of questionable statements, for she had abruptly reverted to her *enfant terrible* mood.

A chain of physical reactions was taking Toni over. It had been close — too close. No passing fear. Her nerves simply weren't up to it, not after her own accident, and they said things came in threes! The idea of a scene with Elissa made her feel weak in the knees, distasteful in the extreme. Very likely only Keith Hammond would be there. A typical bachelor, he was comfortable in male company but serious and shy with the opposite sex. Whatever virtues he possessed as the Nyland family solicitor, on the home front he was no match for Elissa, or indeed any woman.

In silence she entered the house, on striking con-

139

trast to Annette's cavalry charge. She caught sight of herself. She looked a mess – dust and heat and beads of perspiration that spiralled down her back. Her bright tousled hair was blown all about her face. Her blue cotton slacks had a great rent in one knee. Perhaps if she looked hard enough she would vanish miraculously like the mirage. A golden beam of sunlight fell through the door and she thought fright had blown the whole situation up into ridiculous proportions. Sunshine was beautiful, cheering. Nothing sinister could happen in sunlight. Toni tossed up her head, like a thoroughbred filly, a bold, proud gesture.

From the living room came a high shrill squeal – anguish, Elissa's. Toni advanced towards the sound from her manner and the set of her glistening, disarrayed head, as if she were dressed by Givenchy. All four faces turned directly towards her, impressing themselves on her mind. Damon, in the act of standing up – instant authority, a stunning physical elegance even in narrow jeans and a faded cotton shirt. Elissa, shrunken into the armchair, peering round the side, lavender blue eyes staring in unwinking hostility, a spitting cat. Keith Hammond leaning protectively towards her setting up some sort of sympathetic vibration, a muted there, there! Annette, a head full of dusty curls and a shocking pink dress, in her bright green eyes a look of unholy bliss, the centre of the stage, by *any* means. Her audience of adults clustered about her.

Serenely, like a mannequin, Toni walked towards them. "It's not as bad as it looks," she said lightly. "I hope Annette hasn't alarmed you. We had a near accident."

Elissa's voice shattered like glass and as dangerous. "You look dreadful. *Simply dreadful!* "

"Yes, and you look so fresh and nice! "

"What happened?" Damon cut across this exchange, his voice unexpectedly hard. "You're as white as a sheet. If Annette's to be believed at all, you threw a tree at her. Here, sit down! "

It was useless to argue with Damon, useless to stand on her dignity, for he crossed the space between them in two long strides, giving her a little push into a chair. "Any time you care to start. We're all friends here."

"Yes, I know," she said, upset but as outspoken as ever. "It's wonderful to be home. Actually, if you really want to know, we were coming up from the Blue Lady lagoon when one of those old dead gums decided to bite the dust. I can't think now how I came to be alerted to it. There was no warning. It seems like a miracle. I suppose next time I go out, you'd better notify my next of kin."

"There's an idea! "

"You joke about it?" Elissa's voice sailed over the top of Damon's dark drawl. In one concerted movement she swept aside Keith Hammond's restraining hand and lunged towards her avidly-interested-in-the-proceedings child, gathering her into a close, maternal

141

embrace. "My little girl could have been killed, and you joke about it!"

"It's dear of you to leave *me* out. I was there too, Mrs. Nyland," Toni protested.

Almost on cue, overcome by the tortured, touching look in her mother's eyes, Annette burst into hysterical tears, engulfed in the near-atrocity as suggested to her by her mother, screeching until the room was deafened and even Elissa had let go of her.

"Now, now, what's all this to-do?" Clarrie Chase demanded from somewhere close at hand. She walked into the room, wiping her hands on her apron, her forehead knobbling at the decibels of sound. "The way that child carries on is nothing short of disaster!"

"Who wants *your* opinion?" Elissa shrilled, rigid with indignation, her narrow eyes misty with tears of frustration.

"You'd better take it, Mrs. Nyland, while there's still time!" Clarrie retorted, much irritated by all the fuss.

"Clarrie, would you be good enough to take Annette to her room?" Damon requested in a super-polite voice, very much the male, and bored to tears with such stuff. "Give her a bath and settle her down. Especially settle her down!"

"Good as done!" Clarrie said, glancing down at the child.

But Annette was not Annette for nothing. She couldn't do anything halfway. Always extremes — one minute angelic, the next in a rage.

"You beast!" she shouted as Clarrie got a hand to her. "You beastly, wicked old woman!"

Without breaking her stride, Clarrie, a strong woman, tucked the child under her arm and administered a thumping whack on the frantically wriggling bottom. "Don't worry, I won't hurt her," she said calmly. "That was just in the nature of a well-deserved slap – the old boarding school variety from my matron days. It was the 'old' that did it. We all have our vanities!"

"You beast!" Annette continued to shout, scarlet in the face from mingled rage and her head-down position.

"That's enough of that!" Clarrie tucked her still more firmly under her arm, preparing to walk with her.

Elissa was frantic, hitting away Keith Hammond's hand with a vicious side-swipe. "Who is *she* to dictate to my child?"

"Come now, Elissa," Keith Hammond said in a surprisingly firm voice, "you can't condone the child's naughtiness. She had a shock, I know, but there are times when children need punishment, and that was one of them."

Elissa transferred her attention to Toni, a figurine no longer, but a lady panther measuring her cage. "How dare you precipitate this crisis? You've never liked me. I can't think why! I trusted you to look after

143

Annette, now I'll never have a moment's peace again!"
She broke off in her pacing and drew a ragged breath.
"If anything had happened to Annette, because of
you...!"

Toni spoke before she could help herself. "You
must be out of your mind, Mrs. Nyland. I wouldn't
hurt a hair of your silly child's head!"

"How *dare* you!"

Damon turned on his relative with a look of extreme boredom. "You appear to be stuck in a groove,
Elissa. *Calm down!*"

Whatever else he said Toni didn't wait to listen.
She spun on her heel in silent rebellion, unable to bear
it a moment longer. You might as well tell a startled
horse not to bolt! her inner voice cried. Half way
across the terrace she was caught up, hard, pushed
back against the trellised vines.

"Isn't this wildly unorthodox?" she said, wildly
struggling. "All this physical violence?"

"Not with someone like you," he said harshly, reducing her struggles to impotence. "Some women
never create a ripple, but you...!"

"Oh, damn you!" she stormed at him, seared by
conviction. "You don't have to tell me what side
you're on. You'd throw me to the lions for that precious lot. Playing gooseberry to a triangle," she said
rapidly. "What a fool I was! What a job! What a
dreadful mistake!"

"Face up to it, sweetheart!" he said grimly, pinning

her chin and holding her face to him. "If that's the only mistake you've made, you're a very lucky girl!"

She struggled, as stubborn as a dozen contrary donkeys. "No wonder that child is hysterical. Have you seen her mother when she gets into her stride?"

"Be reasonable, Toni," he said, shaking her, losing his own temper. "Whatever Elissa is, I'll take full responsibility. You don't have to worry about it."

"You're damned right I don't!" she said swiftly, her eyes brilliantly dark. "I'm going to seize on any old excuse at all. I'm going home!"

His eyes remained inscrutable, but his touch changed in some subtle, mystifying fashion, melting her bones. "Jealous?" he asked.

The sudden shift in his manner, that spark of devilry, blurred her vision. She couldn't think clearly. She couldn't think at all, and he knew it. A kind of helpless anger rose up in her like a huge silent tide.

"You hit me, my girl," he said tautly, anticipating her, "and I'll turn you over my knee here and now!"

"You're *definitely* mad!"

"Quite! I cheerfully admit it. Just mad enough to call your bluff!"

She was breathing quickly, staring up at him, locked in some savage battle for survival. His hands tightened and her nerves stretched a fraction tighter. "You witch!" he said in an odd undertone. "Even my *mind* has begun to accept the disaster!"

She was swaying towards him, her fingers winding

themselves tightly around his, interlocking, a crackle of electricity, a fork of lightning in a summer sky.

"I say, Damon!" Keith Hammond broke out on to the terrace, his pleasant face agitated. "Would you come? Elissa's had a nasty turn."

"The devil she has!" Lines of irritation were etched about Damon's mouth.

"That's not very lover-like!" Toni taunted him.

"I'll catch up with you," he gritted out, twisting his dark head back to the anxious Hammond. "Go back to her, Keith. I'll get Clarrie. She's a trained nurse as well as everything else. I tell you, the salt-mines beat Savannah hands down these days with hysterical females!"

"You wanted us here!" Toni said recklessly, discretion never a virtue.

He surveyed her for a second in silence, one hand tightly clenched on the side of the trellis, the flash in his eyes as cold as winter steel. Her mouth trembled and her teeth went unpleasantly on edge.

"Oh, Damon!" she said half fearfully, ashamed of her own retreat.

"Don't 'oh, Damon' me," he said in a merciless voice, swinging her high into his arms to hold her against his lean, hard body, leaving her too dumbfounded to speak. Master of the situation. He could do as he pleased. Across the inner court he walked, thrust open her door and threw her on the bed, his green eyes startlingly brilliant.

"The onset of the rains is the target I set myself!" he announced casually with his customary arrogance. "Then look out!"

Her eyes were enormous, highly antagonistic in her warmly tinted face. "Look out yourself!" she said childishly, then flung herself back on the bed.

He glanced down at her in a relaxed, idle way. "It's times like these I realise I'm dealing with an adolescent."

"In a way, yes," she said in a soft shaky voice. "Go along and chat Elissa up. She'll soon put you wise. After today she doesn't strike me as all that much of a paragon!"

"Maybe Elissa hasn't got what you've got!" he said in a light, amused voice, and left her while the wild apricot colour mounted to her cheeks. What a fiery, shattering finish to a terrible day! The only sound was his receding footsteps across the paved court. At the very least, she'd expected fire engines after Elissa's display. One thing was certain, in no circumstances would she be persuaded to stay another day. She blew a wisp of hair away from her mouth, wilful and ardent. In the meantime she would sublimate her feelings. It was her only salvation. Away from Savannah she would be free of these troubled longings, the memory of the shape of a mouth on her own, the imprint of lean, strong hands. Damon Nyland was a forbidden commodity. She would, in time, find someone jolly if dull, but someone who would never expect her to forfeit her privacy and freedom. Savannah's sphere was a jealous and demanding one, she craved to be her own woman. It was monstrous to have Damon Nyland take control of her life.

Almost for a minute Toni gloated on what his future with Elissa would be. For all her shortcomings, she was a rare creature, a narcissist, in psychiatric terms. Then her eyes flashed in sudden disgust. Urge and rhythm in her slender body, she jumped off the bed and ran the shower hard. She would wash her hair. It was always strangely soothing. She'd had all the stimulation she needed. Mandargi was home, a haven, a snug harbour. Who needed the Promised Land?

CHAPTER EIGHT

In the end, Toni agreed to stay until the governess arrived, for Elissa really did suffer a minor brainstorm or the like, that held her captive in her beautiful bedroom for three days; tempted by light delicious meals, a number of cool drinks, a pile of glossies, nothing heavier, until the strength flowed back into her tender limbs. Toni, quick-tempered but warmhearted, was betrayed into a kind of irritated sympathy. Elissa couldn't help what she was. Freed of all financial worry, the necessity of earning her own living and supporting her child, she was forced back on all manner of imaginary illnessess and anxieties to fill in her time. The smallest, transient blemish on her lovely skin was enough to drive her nearly demented, let alone the high winds that sometimes visited Savannah, blowing, blowing, putting her in her own words "around the bend". With the monsoon expected, Toni wondered how on earth she would fare.

The great thing was, Elissa was too fine, too fragile, too delicate to wrestle with the ordinary commonplace things, the right schools, the right clothes, the right friends, the right marriage – the false ideals fed to her since childhood so that she had come to believe in them herself, working tirelessly towards a shallow perfection, not realising that such things in themselves were not reason enough for living. Her husband's tragic death came as a crippling blow, not in the accepted sense of a deep personal loss, a limbo of loneliness and grief, more, the unfairness of it all, for now Elissa would have to stir herself all over again. Her second marriage must eclipse her first. She must find a man who was in every way acceptable. A success by her own, and perhaps more important, by her friends' standards. Anything else was untenable. That he would have to be a man who would fondly deprecate her extravagant follies was understood. Whether he would find it in his heart to lavish loving kindness on little Annette was immaterial. Annette's father had left her well provided for and she would be going to boarding school in any case.

In those few days of Elissa's nervous crisis, Toni came to know Keith Hammond a lot better. Always calm, good-natured, relaxed, he was in every way a solid citizen, at peace with himself and his world, standing four-square on the sanctity of marriage and the legal profession. As he confided to Toni in his pleasant, uneffusive way, his early goals and ambitions had prevented his forming a permanent alliance beyond a spot of calf love at university when he was desperately smitten and equally desperately disillusioned. But now, in his early forties, a nice age for a man, on a decently elevated plateau of material success, he wanted marriage. He wanted Elissa. No names were used, but he wanted Elissa. In fact it was abundantly clear to his audience of one that he wanted nothing more out of life than to dedicate himself to Elissa's happiness.

If Toni thought him wanting in taste and good judgment, she gave not the slightest sign of it to plague him. He was, in any event, a *kindly* man, ready to shed his bounty on young Annette, who surprisingly smiled whenever they met. But day by day on Savannah he fretted. It was a gruelling business to have to watch his friend and treasured client effortlessly fascinate the woman he loved. For without Elissa he had come to believe life would be as arid as the Simpson desert. It was common knowledge anyway that he had as good as chased her all over three

States and on to Savannah, on what appeared to many to be a senseless mission, but of course Toni, who agreed, never so much as hinted any such thing. In fact, she subtly encouraged him in his fantasies, if only from a mistaken idea of good-heartedness.

If anyone was to blame, it was Damon. Damon was Damon — always there, always his own dynamic self, lounging in doorways, hands thrust casually into his pockets, green eyes able, in one second, to pick up the threads of any situation. Never anything else but at ease everywhere, his old mocking self, and Toni wished over and over that she could tell him to go to the devil. He was maddening. She could explode like a firecracker just thinking about him. His insolence, his arrogance — so smug! So certain he could manipulate her like he did so many others. He really had a re-markable talent for mesmerising people who could be of use to him. For Damon used people, constantly, selfishly, shamelessly. Never mind if they loved it, hanging on his every word as if it were of paramount importance. But a friend? Who could ever make a friend of a tiger? Worst of all, he had the power to hurt her. She couldn't think of him without melo-drama and histrionics. It was only natural, she sup-posed. She was a woman. She loved him and she was jealous, her heart stormy, filled with self-contempt for her fury of hurt pride.

So he preferred Elissa? What of it? In his com-pany Elissa came to sparkling life, her silvery laugh echoing round and round the walls of Savannah. Toni couldn't bolster herself with the thought that Damon also found her attractive. She certainly hadn't flung herself at his head. The attraction was very real and it was a tiny stir of life that moved her despite herself. He hadn't deceived her in any way. She had only herself to blame if she attached more importance than it deserved to a few misses. If she loved him, as was her way, with everything she *was*, it was her own fault again. She didn't regret it, for if she had it would have been a denial of herself.

She could even forgive him loving Elissa. She was, after all, an assured beauty, sophisticated and knowledgeable. Love was not logical or even reasonable, and definitely not fair. No justice anywhere. The most unlikely people found a smooth path to it. Love, the elixir of life, yet it took precious little to make it evaporate. Love was a cage, for she had the unhappy notion that for her, from now on, all men would wear the same face – Damon's. She knew she was hurt and the hurt would go on for a long time, but somehow she would make out. Back on Mandargi she might be free of his bright tyranny, splendid and arrogant, the devastating flashes of humour that made him so very attractive. She was young. She would try to be happy. But she would never forget Damon whatever her destiny.

Another week went by, very fast, so that Toni later thought of it as a raving nightmare. Her controls were beginning to slip and she knew it. It was sheer torture to see Elissa's hand hovering, then lingering on Damon's arm, her shining small head thrown back to meet the sardonic indulgence, never devilry, she seemed to call forth from him. No one could ever deny they made a handsome couple, an almost perfect physical foil, as arresting in its fashion as a white camellia on a black jacket. All this Toni took in at her own risk; her better judgment seemed to have no power at all, for it was a breathtaking, piercing, bittersweet delight to be near him, at any cost.

Even on Savannah with its limitless horizons, Damon Nyland was a man separate from his background. He never merged, never lost impact, but stood out clearly, very vital, very much the individual, a man with an exciting image and straightforwardly masculine. So each day Toni determined on a course of self-razzle-dazzle. She rose early, swam a few lengths of the pool, then planned a jaunt for herself and Annette. A manoeuvre designed to keep them out of the house for long hours and from under Elissa's narrow feet. But they *did* see a lot of the property and once they hid in a feathery grove of acacias along one of the tree-lined gullies watching the rufous-topped brolgas dance their quadrille on the reed flats. It was a beautiful visual impression that left its mark on both of their memories.

But each night in her room, long after she had settled Annette for the night, Toni reverted to some mysterious underworld of secret and impossible dreams. It was foolish, but she couldn't help it, her feeling was so complete and profound. She brushed her hair facing the mirror, her eyes half closed and dreamy, the light sheening the silken lids. From her long hours in the sun, her skin had turned from cream to a warm peach. She used little make-up and rarely got out of shirts and flared slacks except for dinner at night when she changed into a simple dress, one that offered no competition for Elissa's meticulously worked-on perfection. What she didn't realise was that her unadorned face had distinction and character. Her mirror image never revealed the fresh, living face, the gleaming highlights in hair that so emphatically framed her modern, contemporary young beauty. She never really saw herself as others saw her – the fine dark eyebrows, silky black lashes, thick and spiky, the fronded brilliance of dark irises with their gleams of shifting light. If there was knowledge and experience in Elissa's jacaranda gaze, there was a delicate innocence in Toni's eyes for all their touch of temperament.

The same week-end Cathy Tennant, the new governess, was due in, the whole Nyland clan arrived for a general meeting and celebration combined, for one of their senior members had been elected to the Senate. They flew in, en masse, and almost immediately started in to a series of business discussions for the men, gossip sessions for the women, who were rigidly excluded with no more expected of them than to be pretty and pleasant, but a lot of fun was had in between times. Jaunts round the property, picnics and swimming and riding; the pool was very popular, polocrosse for the men, a display of camp drafting, cutting out cattle, breaking in the best of the brumbies, wheeling, galloping, biting and lashing, snorting and pawing the ground and the inevitable rough riding from every hand on the station, buck-jumping, with the horse, Salvation Jane, emerging the exclusive reigning champion, ready and willing to throw the gamest challenger, to the sun and the wind, then the ground.

The Saturday evening the whole of Savannah would come to life with a gala party, semi-formal for the family, gaily informal for the station employees and their families and anyone who cared to come for hundreds of miles around. A great many cared, and they all came, pitching tents under the massed shade of the eucalyptus ready for a night under the blossoming stars.

So far as the Nylands were concerned, they were pretty much as Toni expected – sleek and gregarious, very "family", the young ones trendy in all kinds of fabulous gear; moving, talking, swimming, riding with practised skill and grace, the perfect assurance a great deal of money seemed to bring. The men were very friendly, very appreciative of a woman's good looks, the women a mixture of curious-wary-friendly with the occasional downright patronising, independent of family status, for the Senator's lady was far and away the most charming.

It was Cathy Tennant, the governess, who was the real surprise – a small girl, neat and fine-boned, fiercely red hair, deep slate-coloured eyes, a pixie, not pretty face, that was still very pleasing, if not endearing, a fair share of freckles, and a smile like a sunburst, a sudden radiance that people found themselves waiting for like some heart-warming revelation. It revealed the true Cathy, a bright self-reliant girl, but soft too and very funny. Toni took to her at once. A natural empathy was established at once with a little humorous aside on the degree of redness to which hair could attain, from Toni's rose-bronze to Cathy's almost burnt-orange. When she heard there was to be a party that night, her smile broke out afresh, her gaiety and youthful high spirits ready to embrace the world. If she emerged from her interview with Elissa that bit subdued, she soon picked up again, to fire a volley of questions at Toni, who sat on the end of her bed, watching Cathy shake out her clothes and hang them away in the long built-in wardrobe. She was thrilled with her surroundings and didn't fail to say so in her bubbling, beguiling fashion.

"Any words of advice on how to handle Mrs. *Elissa* Nyland?" she inquired, gyrating with a party frock.

"God, no!" Toni said so emphatically. The other

girl looked startled, then broke into peals of laughter. "Then we'll just have to have a little 'think' session, won't we? Now, Mr. Nyland, Mr. *Damon* Nyland, that is, there's such a lot of them, he's a super man, isn't he? A great chunk of purest gold. Gorgeous! I thought they were only like that in films. All that tall, dark, handsome bit really grabs you, doesn't it? Makes you go weak at the knees. He swung me down from the plane, you know. A delicate adagio, wafting through space. All the good times, come at once!"

"Elissa saw him first!" Toni contributed soberly.

This brought Cathy to a rapid halt. "Yo-ho-diddly-di-do! A point that had not previously occurred to me." She pursed her bottom lip. "So that's the way of it! Just as well you told me, or I'd have set out like Columbus on uncharted seas!"

"Well, it was short notice, I admit!" Toni smiled, "but *do* decide on my advice. I'm not saying it won't be hard, a fight all the way. But look at the broad pattern. I'll introduce you to my brother. He's a gay bachelor, but very well trained!"

"Your brother, you say? That's very generous of you!" Cathy twirled lightly, all attention. "Tell me, does he look just a little like you? If he does, my stay is complete!"

"He *does*!" Toni smiled, "but aside from that aspect of the matter, he's very nice. Very nice indeed! Flower-blue eyes, utterly wasted on a man!"

"How could you *mean* that?" Cathy cornered her

157

with her eyes. "That little 'ole statement won't bear closer examination. Know what I mean?"

"*Yes*," Toni said, suddenly assailed by a vision. Her heart leapt, but she tried to appear calm, keeping her head down until the moment of danger had passed.

"Your brother, you say," Cathy was bubbling on happily. "When do I meet him?"

"On your first week-end off, if you like. We'd love to have you. We lease Mandargi, another cattle property to the south-west, from Mr. Nyland. It's no Savannah, but we don't endure any economic hardships."

"Is such a thing possible in this country?" Cathy whirled to face her, speaking with unabashed sincerity. "Thank you so much, Toni, I'd love to come. I'm really getting my money's worth here. New Zealand was very kind to me, so friendly, and such glorious scenery, but Australia! Why, you can throw in an extra dimension. It's so *big*! You can go on for ever and still not get anyplace. That's the first thing that strikes you. Why, Queensland alone would swallow up the whole of Western Europe and still leave the Pacific coastline and all the off-shore islands. I'd say the Great Barrier Reef was my favourite beauty spot in the whole world, and I've been through all the glamorous places. Working, of course. Money is always gratifying!" She folded a silk scarf and put it away in a drawer, then broke into an improvised song:

"Australia, I love you, I do, I do,
I love the blue sky above you
and your sea of sapphire blue!"

"Cripes, mate, I love your enthusiasm!" Toni smiled and affected a laconic drawl. "In fact, I think you're absolutely splendid!"

"You're more splendid than I," Cathy protested, judging the completely satisfactory inner springs of the bed.

"Not at all! I will willingly concede we're equally splendid!" Toni bounced up and down, becoming involved despite herself.

"All right. Just whatever you say, dear." Cathy collapsed back into an armchair, flushed with her exertions. "This is a super house, isn't it?" she said with great conviction. "Naturally I took the trouble to enquire into the more significant facts of the Nyland biography. It must be really something to have so much of everything you never have to question yourself or your way of life. You just *are*. It's so unexpected, too, to find a place like this in the middle of nowhere. The house and the furnishings and the *paintings* and all those gorgeous bits and pieces I can't wait to feast my eyes on. In fact, if I didn't know I was in the middle of the Australian bush, I'd think I was back home on one of the big estates. The landed gentry and all that. I mean, he's like a bloomin' feudal lord or something, a slice of the past. It's not fair.

I tell you, it's not fair!"

"I believe he worked very hard for what he's got!" Toni said magnanimously, striving to be fair. "It wasn't until a great many of his ideas were proven before the rest of the family came in with the backing for the big ventures."

"Money makyth money!" Cathy intoned. "It's sort of inevitable, isn't it? Half their luck! The Lady Elissa is very *grand*. Pure and fine and a great frontal attack. A thousand questions crowd to my tongue, but I know I shouldn't ask them. Strike that one off the record. I don't want to blot my copybook this first day off, but I feel I've known you a hundred years, and so forth. Interesting, is it not? Your people didn't pass through the British Isles, by any chance?"

"Both my grandmothers came from Ireland, if that's any good to you."

"Yes, I've heard of Ireland," Cathy said, her dark grey eyes dancing. "And they tore up their roots to come here?"

"They felt they owed it to their husbands, I imagine. They were resident in Australia at the time." Toni screwed up her eyes surveying the quaint, pixie face in front of her. "You don't look unlike the 'little people' yourself! Tell me, what are you wearing this evening? That taffeta tartan has great potential."

"This one?" Cathy went to the wardrobe and twitched out the long skirt of a halter-necked number in different shades of violet and lilac. "I thought it

160

was a bit violent myself, for a *first* evening. One mustn't overdo it."

"No, I like it," Toni repeated. "And I'm hyper-sensitive!"

"Well, it has had a lot of mileage," Cathy said thoughtfully, smoothing her flaming aura. "Which just goes to prove I like it myself. Important for a girl. Never mind what the men think. Now, what about you? What are you wearing? Not that it matters when you look like a cross between Audrey Hepburn and Ali MacGraw."

"Come and see what you think. I hate everything!" Toni got up off the bed and led the way along the terrace to her own room, where the girls fell into a discussion on the possibilities among Toni's very limited wardrobe. They both agreed she could look very much better than she probably would with what was on hand, but there was little they could do. They were not of a size. Cathy was a "twiggy" girl and Toni was three inches taller and a different shape. But what did it matter? Elissa, undoubtedly, would steal the show, with the rest of the Nyland women offering some pretty heavy challenge. They were the lilies of the field, and both girls were sensible of the distinction.

As a general maxim, Toni had long since accepted, things do not always work out as planned. Life was full of surprises, whether desirable or not, and when they were pleasant, it helped a lot. In this way she dressed for the party that evening with a feeling inside her approaching elation. A kind of triple glow, for now she had a new friend and a true friend in Cathy, one who was destined to become her lifelong confidante: Damon had withheld until the last minute the much appreciated gesture of flying Paul in, and as a consequence of having a thoughtful and far-seeing brother she now wore her one and only dazzle dress, a Jean Patou copy and an extravagance from the old days. It became her like no other – a slither of amber paillettes on a bronze silk ground, twinkling, glittering, throwing off the most beautiful bloom on her face and her bare shoulders and throat. It was very simple in cut, being little more than a slip, but it was very sophisticated and she applied herself with great diligence to making the most of her hair and her make-up, till she blossomed into something very special indeed. She stared into the mirror with a gathering excitement and what she saw there gave her confidence.

"My, you've changed!" she said to herself. "Why, I scarcely know you. It's a long, long time since you've looked like that!"

Almost eight months, she deduced, falling to musing on the exact date. Ever since then she had dressed for comfort, not fashion. A little embarrassed, she tried to resurrect that evening with Martin. Goodhearted Martin! Suffering fools gladly, always turning the other cheek, nursing the one drink all evening,

. . . hen I arrived. It was all I could do not to shove . . . ad first into the fishpond on the offchance!"

. . . flicker of astonishment staggered her eyes. She . . . completely confused, clutching at remembrance.

. . . e Elissa into the fishpond? That didn't add up in . . . iment or gallantry. There was something sadly . . . iss here.

"I fell," she said at last, slowly, distinctly. "I lost . . . y balance. No question about it, I must be bumble- . . . ooted!"

"Bravo!" he said in terse sarcasm. "You're a brave one. I'd like to know what she'd been saying to you, all the same."

She didn't answer, though he paused, waiting for her to go on. "Toni?"

They weighed each other carefully, utterly intent, the one on the other. Her eyes were black and velvet through the thick density of her lashes, and evasive. "I didn't like it then and I like it less now," she volunteered, "but I'm not saying! It was just a bad dream. It might be a good idea if *you* go away, though!" she added unsteadily, avoiding his expressive gaze.

"Why?" His gaze pinned her down.

"Well, heavens, you shouldn't be here!" she pointed out, her heart thumping sadly.

"I'll be where I damned well please!" he said with complete arrogance, on course again as the master of limitless horizons. "Besides, you'd better get used to it – seeing me here whenever you wake up!" He looked

187

into her enormous eyes, startled and unbelieving. "I hope you don't mind, not that it makes a great deal of difference."

The cadences of his familiar voice fell on her stunned ears. "You are *real*?" she said faintly. "You're not a wish fantasy? I'm still not dreaming?"

"No!" he said lightly, and his lean brown fingers twined through her own. "Here we are, together again. Real people. Hearts and minds. These odd things happen in life, but if you're none too sure . . ." He bent his dark head and dropped a hard kiss on her mouth that was a mixture of desire, reassurance and utter possession.

Life surged through her veins and colour swept into her face, lending her a breathtaking beauty. "I love you!" she said aloud, when she thought she had cried it out silently.

"That's what worries me!" he murmured, and ran a tantalising hand down her cheek. "It's a big responsibility!"

"I mean it!"

"I know you do."

She turned her face into his hand and kissed the palm. "I love you, Damon. When did you find out?"

"Oh . . ." he narrowed his eyes thoughtfully. "The first time I kissed you, perhaps. On Mandargi, certainly. You were just what I expected — a fireball, but very sweet nevertheless. I knew it was all over for me, though I struggled a bit as a matter of form. I don't